Library

St. Olaf College

Northfield, Minn.

the Ocean

A **SCIENTIFIC AMERICAN** *Book*

the Ocean

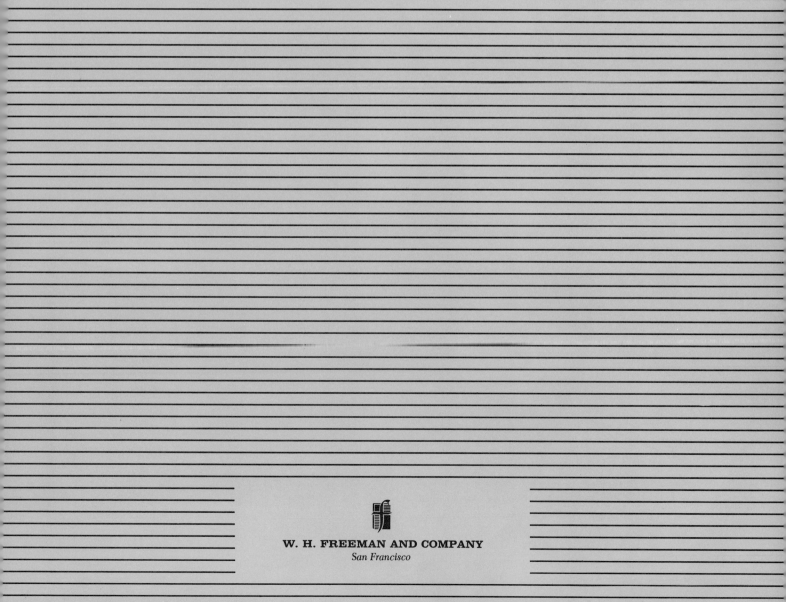

W. H. FREEMAN AND COMPANY
San Francisco

GC 11
f. 024

Copyright © 1969 by Scientific American, Inc.
All rights reserved. No part of this book may
be reproduced in any form without permission in
writing from the publisher, except by a
reviewer, who may quote brief passages and
reproduce not more than three illustrations in a
review to be printed in a magazine or newspaper.

The ten chapters in this book originally appeared
as articles in the September 1969 issue of
Scientific American. Each is available as a
separate Offprint (Numbers 879–888) from
W. H. Freeman and Company, 660 Market Street,
San Francisco, California 94104.

Library of Congress Catalogue Card Number: 71–102897

Standard Book Number: 7167 0998–8 (cloth)
            7167 0997–X (paper)

Printed in the United States of America

9 8 7 6 5 4 3 2 1

Contents

266684

Foreword

No book can hold between its covers the unbounded ocean: nonetheless, this book deserves its title. It portrays the ocean as it has become known to science during the past two decades. Roger Revelle, in the first chapter, calls this period "one of the great ages of exploration." While the space spectaculars of the two superpowers held public attention, the work of a few oceanographers was gaining for all men "a new level of understanding of their planetary home."

Oceanographic vessels equipped with echo-sounding and seismic-recording gear, magnetometers, and gravimeters have traversed empty ocean wildernesses, charting the topography and substructure of substantial stretches of the ocean floor. The now emergent map of this concealed two-thirds of the surface of the earth has brought into view a major feature with the same grand dimensions as the continents and the ocean itself. This is the 40,000-mile-long continuous mountain range, rifted along much of its length, that winds nearly twice around the globe under the ocean. As Edward Bullard and H. W. Menard show, the discovery of the mid-ocean ridge has set off in geology a revolution comparable to that which turned physics around at the beginning of this century and to the revolution in the life sciences that has followed the cracking of the genetic code. The once disreputable notion of continental drift is now suddenly installed at the center of an elaborating general theory of geology.

From sampling and from photographic surveys of the continental shelves and the abyssal bottom it has been determined that much of the soluble mineral wealth leached from the rock and soils of the continents has precipitated out on the ocean floor and lies there for the dredging. This and related findings have inspired fantasies in the Forty-niner and Klondike mode. Great industrial corporations have ordained "oceanology" departments, and their advertisements have featured frog men and little yellow submarines. Sobering economic second thoughts, reviewed here by Edward Wenk, Jr., are now showing that the mineral riches of the ocean are too thinly distributed, both on the bottom and in solution, to permit profitable recovery by known technologies and at prevailing prices. Offshore oil fields, however, now supply a significant and growing percentage of the world's oil, thanks to the development of the sophisticated and daring methods described by Willard Bascom.

The story of "food from the sea" has had the same plot. Malthusian anxiety about world population growth conjured up compensating expectations of a scientific re-enactment of the miracle of the loaves and fishes. But life in the sea, as S. J. Holt shows, is already heavily exploited and, at some points, dangerously threatened by human appetites, and is too thinly dispersed in the water to permit application of methods that would increase yield significantly. It is only in the estuaries and near-shore shallows that agricultural practices may develop substantial new protein supplies. These waters must be rescued, however, from pollution.

Closer inspection of the moon and of the moonlike surface of Mars has given men a new appreciation of water as the distinguishing feature of their planet. Life originated in the ocean, and living cells are 98 percent salt water. The ocean is a single great ecosystem. It is far more susceptible to harm by careless exploitation than the land. This is a good occasion to recall, therefore, that science gives us not only technology but *science,* not only control of nature but understanding!

The chapters in this book were first published as articles in the September, 1969, issue of *Scientific American.* This was the twentieth in the series of annual single-topic issues published by the magazine. The editors herewith express appreciation to their colleagues at W. H. Freeman and Company, the book-publishing affiliate of *Scientific American,* for the enterprise that has made the contents of this issue so speedily available in book form.

THE EDITORS*

September, 1969

* BOARD OF EDITORS: Gerard Piel (Publisher), Dennis Flanagan (Editor), Francis Bello (Associate Editor), Philip Morrison (Book Editor), Jonathan B. Piel, John Purcell, James T. Rogers, Armand Schwab, Jr., C. L. Stong, Joseph Wisnovsky

I

The Ocean

The Ocean

ROGER REVELLE

An introduction to a study of the ocean, with special reference to man's advancing utilization of the ocean and his new understanding of how the present oceans were created

I grew up not far from the ocean and have lived most of my adult life near the seashore. The ocean holds me in an enduring spell. Part of the spell comes from mystery—the fourfold mystery of the shoreline, the surface, the horizon and the timeless motion of the sea. The thin, moving line between land and water on an open coast presents a nearly impenetrable wall. The ships and fishing boats I watch from my living-room window exist in a separate world, as remote as another planet. Below the surface there is a multitude of living things, darting and watching, living and dying; theirs is an alien world I cannot see and can hardly imagine. At the horizon, where my line of sight touches the edge of the great globe itself, I watch ships slowly disappear, first the hulls and then the tall masts, bound on voyages to unknown ports 10,000 miles away. From beyond the horizon come the waves that break rhythmically on the beach, sounding now loud, now soft, as they did long before I was born and as they will in the far future. The restless, ever changing ocean is timeless on the scale of my life, and this also is a mystery.

Part of the ocean spell comes from the interplay of light and reflection between the sea and the sky, the track of sunlight on the water and the pale or rosy colors of clouds. It was these that fascinated the greatest of all English painters, J. M. W. Turner, and inspired part of Debussy's tone poem "La Mer." In order to observe and study the infinite variety of color patterns over the ocean, Turner found a house by the sea in east Kent. He allowed the natives to think he was an eccentric sea captain named Puggy Booth, who even in retirement could not stop looking at the sea.

The ocean has an impact on all our senses: the unique sea smell, the crashing sound of breakers, the glitter of waves dancing under the sun and the moon, the feel of spindrift blowing across one's face, the salty, bitter taste of the water. Yet the spell of the ocean is more than mystery and sensory delight. Part of it must come from outside the senses, from half-forgotten memories and images beyond imagining, deep below the surface of consciousness.

Being an oceanographer is not quite the same as being a professional sailor. Oceanographers have the best of two worlds—both the sea and the land. Yet many of them, like many sailors, find it extraordinarily satisfying to be far from the nearest coast on one of the small, oily and uncomfortable ships of their trade, even in the midst of a vicious storm, let alone on one of those wonderful days in the Tropics when the sea and the air are smiling and calm. I think the chief reason is that on shipboard both the past and the future disappear. Little can be done to remedy the mistakes of yesterday; no planning for tomorrow can reckon with the unpredictability of ships and the sea. To live in the present is the essence of being a seaman.

The work of an oceanographer, however, is inextricably related to time. To understand the present ocean he must reconstruct its history, and to test and use his understanding he needs to be able to predict—both what he will find by new observations and future events in the sea.

Over the past two decades there has been a marvelous increase in our understanding of the geological history of the ocean. This has come about chiefly through wide-ranging exploration of the earth under the sea by investigators of many countries, using a variety of new instruments and powerful new methods. I believe that in times to come these 20 years when men gained a new level of understanding of their planetary home will be thought of as one of the great ages of exploration.

In the wealth of new knowledge there is no discovery more paradoxical than this: the ocean floor is younger than the ocean. Below the ancient waters the sediments and the underlying rocks are

MAN CONTEMPLATES THE OCEAN in this detail of a seascape painted in 1865 by the American artist James McNeill Whistler on the beach near the English Channel town of Trouville in France. The title of the painting is *Harmony in Blue and Silver: Trouville*. It is reproduced with the kind permission of the Isabella Stewart Gardner Museum in Boston.

constantly renewed. An almost continuous ridge 40,000 miles long and several hundred miles wide, rifted along much of its length by deep valleys and broken by numerous fractures, lies in the central part of the oceans—a structure on the same planetary scale as the oceans and continents themselves. Magnetic, thermal and seismic observations show that near the summit of the ridge new rock wells up from the mantle below and slowly moves outward across the ocean basins. Along some margins of the ocean the spreading ocean floor moves the adjacent continents; elsewhere the floor plunges downward in deep trenches and disappears into the earth's interior [see "The Deep-Ocean Floor," by H. W. Menard, page 53].

The simplicity and grandeur of this hypothesis of sea-floor spreading has caught the imagination of earth scientists throughout the world. As a result, as Sir Edward Bullard says in the article following this one: "We are in the middle of a rejuvenating process in geology comparable to the one that physics experienced in the 1890's and to the one that is now in progress in molecular biology."

In this same brief period, in pursuit of both scientific and economic or military objectives, man has acquired a new freedom of operation in the third dimension of the ocean. Below the forbidding mystery of the surface, developing technology gives access to greater and greater depths and to the resources awaiting discovery and exploitation there. Offshore wells now supply a fifth of the world's oil and gas. The value of their output is already equal to half the product of the fisheries and to a fourth of the value of the services rendered by the freighters and tankers that ply the sea-lanes. Anticipation of still greater yields has brought an ominous extension of claims of national sovereignty [see "The Ocean and Man," by Warren S. Wooster, page 121]. Beyond the narrow limits of the territorial seas, established by the range of cannon in earlier days, the 1958 Geneva Convention on the Continental Shelf gives a coastal state the exclusive right to exploit the seabed out to a depth of 200 meters or "beyond that limit, to where the depth of the superjacent waters admits of the exploitation of the natural resources of the said area."

Some international lawyers have interpreted this provision to mean that as deep-water technology advances the coastal states will be able to extend their jurisdiction out to the midpoint of the ocean basins. The long-run consequences of such a division of the ocean into national territories are appalling to contemplate. They would constitute a *reductio ad absurdum* of the concept of nation-states.

Even today the ocean both divides and links the nations of mankind. In the past the fate of many peoples was shaped by the sea. The list of these peoples includes the Phoenicians, who are said to have been the first seamen to dare to sail at night, guided by the North Star; the sea kings of Crete; the Athenians; the Norsemen of the Middle Ages and their nearly antipodal contemporaries the Polynesians; the Genoans and Venetians of the late Middle Ages; the Portuguese, the Spaniards and the Dutch during the Renaissance, and the English from the 16th to the 20th centuries.

All the sea peoples shared several characteristics. In the beginning their populations were small and their lands were poor. If they were to prosper, it had to be by commerce and trade, or by finding new lands to conquer and colonize. All were courageous, ingenious, rapacious and ruthless. All were filled with a spirit of curiosity and a drive for discovery, and this was probably their unique quality. Although some of them built great empires, none lasted in any real sense for more than a few hundred

DEPTH (METERS)	0 TO 200	2,000 TO 4,000	6,000 TO 8,000
	200 TO 2,000	4,000 TO 6,000	8,000 AND BELOW

VASTNESS OF THE WORLD OCEAN is emphasized in this map, which is referred to by cartographers as a homolographic equal-area projection. The sea covers some 140 million

years. Their home resources were inadequate to maintain the burdens they had assumed, and the overseas outposts were without roots and unstable.

The energy, will and creative power of the sea peoples are symbolized in the design of their ships. Consider the marvelous wooden ships of the Vikings, as represented by the ship found so remarkably intact in 1880 in the burial mound at Gokstad in Norway. In contrast to the static or soaring grandeur of the structures of stone built by the nations that are rooted in the land, the Gokstad ship is mobile and light. She is only 78 feet long, about the length of Columbus' *Niña;* her draft is no more than three feet and her planks are less than an inch thick. Her seaworthiness was proved for modern skeptics when an exact replica crossed the Atlantic under oars and sail in 1893. The carved ornamentation of the prows of many of the Viking ships somewhat resembles the adornment of old stave churches that still stand in Norway, but it has a rhythmic, moving pattern that leaps forward toward the unknown. Its delicate sophistication reminds us that on some of their long voyages the Vikings sailed down the Volga and across the Caspian Sea to Persia, returning home laden with exotic treasures and new ideas. On another expedition they carved a runic rhyme on a marble lion at Apollo's sacred island of Delos.

The lines of the best sailing ships were always functional, designed to give the combination of speed, sea-keeping ability, cargo and passenger space and, if necessary, protection against enemies that was needed for a particular trade. Speed depended not only on the ship's resistance to the water and on its effective sail area but also on the hull form and the rigging that would allow laying a course as close as possible to the wind, and on the length at the waterline, which

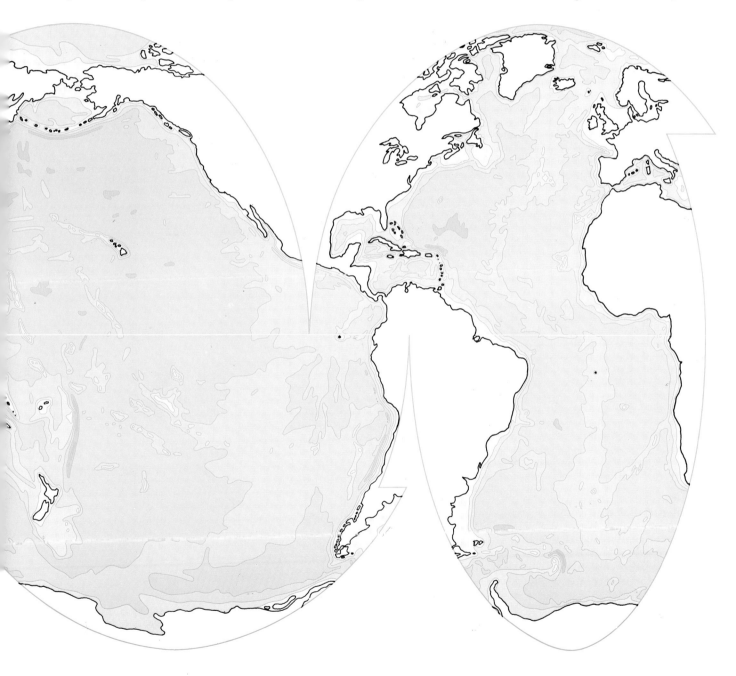

square miles, or 71 percent of the earth's surface, leaving only about 29 percent for the continental masses and lesser islands. The average depth of the sea is two and a half miles. Hence the total volume of water in the ocean is roughly 350 million cubic miles.

determined the velocity of the waves made by the ship. The variety of ways in which the different sea peoples solved these problems, in accordance with their particular needs and available materials, is a constant delight to the amateur of sailing ships. When these diverse vessels were under full sail in a fresh breeze, how beautiful they must have been!

Fortunately the beauty of sailing ships under way has always had wide popular appeal, and numerous realistic paintings and drawings still exist, although almost all the ships themselves have long since disappeared. The splendor of the sea in those days is mirrored in the slim grace of a modern high-masted sailing yacht, sailing full and by or running free under a spinnaker; this must be one of the finest sights ever seen by a sailorman. Yet even a tramp freighter or an oceanographic vessel, when viewed from a distance, has a certain dignity.

Although ships are always feminine and many of them, from *Queen Elizabeth 2* to Italian fishing boats, have been named after women, the ocean world is preeminently a masculine one. Sailors talk a good deal about the lovely, pliant girls they are going to visit in the next port, and mermaids, sea nymphs and sirens have filled their fantasies, but they usually take a dim view of women on shipboard. Because the ocean is a cruel mistress she demands the masculine virtues of courage and strength rather than

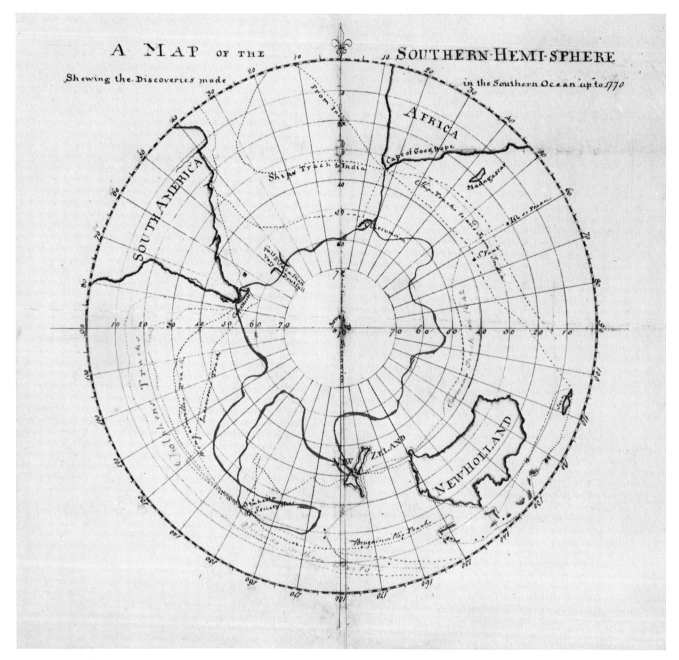

EXPLORATION OF THE OCEAN is symbolized by this map of the Southern Hemisphere drawn by Captain James Cook and enclosed in his memorandum to Lord Sandwich dated 6 February 1772. The strong continuous line (yellow in the original) indicates the route Cook proposed for his second circumnavigation of the globe. The tracks of earlier navigators are shown by dotted lines. One of these lines (labeled "Endeavour's Track") shows the route followed by Cook in his first great voyage of discovery, which lasted from 1768 to 1771. On these two voyages Cook proved the nonexistence of Terra Australis, a huge imaginary continent that for hundreds of years had been thought to cut off the Southern Ocean beyond about 50 degrees south latitude. Although he encountered many icebergs near the southern limits of his track and deduced that they must have broken off from very large glaciers on a land mass beyond the Antarctic Circle, Cook never glimpsed Antarctica itself except in his imagination. The original of this map, which measures about 12 inches on a side, was photographed at the Public Library of New South Wales in Sydney, Australia.

the feminine ones of compassion and sensitivity. From a human standpoint, therefore, the ocean is only a half-world, and this fact has profoundly affected men's relationships to the sea.

To sense the character of life at sea under sail one must listen to the chanteys sailors sang to help haul in heavy lines and the "forecastle songs" that whiled away the dogwatch hours in the evening. In these days of disciplined labor workmen toil in concentrated silence. Seamen on the old sailing ships howled and yelled and sang at their work. As Richard Henry Dana wrote in *Two Years before the Mast,* "A song is as necessary to sailors as a drum and fife to soldiers. They can't pull in time or pull with a will without it." There were the short drag chanteys:

> *Haul on the bowline, our bully ship's*
> *a-rolling,*
> *Haul on the bowline, the bowline haul!*

Halyard chanteys were for hoisting the sail and catting the anchor:

> *O blow the man down, bullies,*
> *Blow the man down!*
> *To me way—aye, blow the man down...*
> *Give me some time to*
> *Blow the man down!*

Capstan chanteys were for steady pushing on the capstan bars when the anchor was being weighed or the ship warped:

> *Oh say was you ever in Rio Grande?*
> *Way, you Rio!...*
> *Sing fare ye well, my pretty young girls,*
> *For we're bound to the Rio Grande.*

Forecastle songs were often ballads, as familiar on the land as on the sea. Among them is "The High Barbaree," which tells how a British ship sank a pirate:

> *Blow high, blow low, 'cause slow*
> *sailed we,*
> *Look ahead, look astern, look*
> *to windward and to lee*
> *Cruising down along the coast*
> *of the High Barbaree.*

The relationship between nations and the sea has often been described in terms of national sea power. The American naval theorist Alfred Thayer Mahan, in his classic work *The Influence of Sea Power upon History, 1660–1783,* held that the sea power of a state rested on three things: the production of manufactured

MANILA GALLEON was a remarkably seaworthy ship that for 250 years (from 1565 to 1815) was used to make round-trip voyages between the Spanish colonies in Mexico and the Philippines. Curiously the Spaniards never discovered the Hawaiian Islands, although they sailed both north and south of them. Hawaii was finally discovered by Cook in 1778.

goods in the home country for overseas trade, commerce across the seas in its own ships, and colonies or dependent states on the farther shore to provide safe ports and goods for exchange, usually raw materials to be brought back to the home country for fabrication into finished products. The function of a navy was to advance all three elements of sea power. By dominating the sea the navy protected the homeland from invasion and ensured that wars would be fought on other people's territory, while production proceeded unimpeded at home. The navy guarded the nation's merchant ships and drove the ships of other nations off the ocean. It helped in the acquisition of colonies and ensured their subsequent docility by transporting and supplying troops and administrators and by preventing other states from interfering in these activities.

The Battle of Salamis is a famous example of naval protection of the home country. Greece was saved from Persian conquest by the "wooden walls" of Athens, and Xerxes flogged the sea that had betrayed him. The subsequent organization at Athens of the Delian league (through which many of the Greek islands and maritime cities at first contributed to a common treasury on the sacred island of Delos and were later forced to submit to Athenian rule) illustrates the use of a navy to acquire and control overseas dependencies. At the same time

Athens greatly expanded her commerce throughout the Mediterranean world, thus developing the second of Mahan's three elements of sea power, and for a few decades she enjoyed a golden age.

The tragedy of the Carthaginian brothers Hannibal and Hasdrubal was chosen by Mahan to illustrate the protective role of sea power. At the time of the Second Punic War between Rome and Carthage, although the Mediterranean Sea had not yet become the Roman *mare nostrum,* Roman fleets had effective control of the Adriatic, Tyrrhenian and Sardinian seas, of the eastern coast of Spain as far south as the mouth of the Ebro and of the northern and eastern coast of Sicily as far down as Syracuse. Hannibal's fleet was not strong enough to enable him to invade Italy by sea. From Carthage through his supply base in southern Spain he launched his forces overland across Gaul and the Alps. On this march he lost 33,000 of the 60,000 veteran soldiers with whom he started.

In spite of these losses Hannibal managed to score a series of brilliant military successes in Italy, but his army slowly wasted away because the Roman control of the sea denied him replacements. His ally Philip of Macedon was unable to land any soldiers in Italy, and Carthage could provide only occasional support by sea. Finally Hasdrubal managed to cross the Pyrenees at their extreme western end and to press on through Gaul

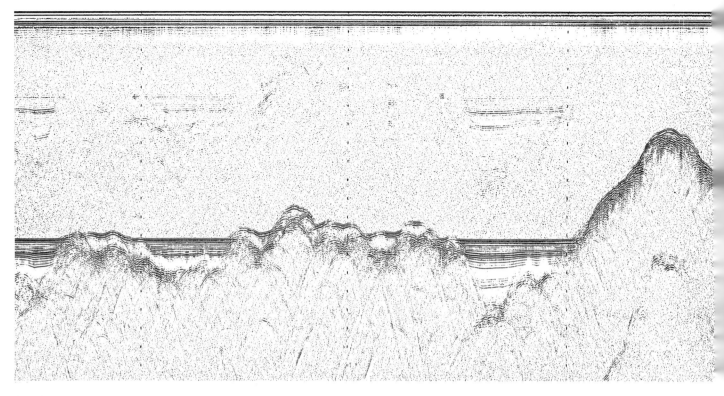

SEISMIC PROFILE on the following six pages shows a continuous cross-sectional view of the geological structure of the deep-ocean floor in the vicinity of the mid-Atlantic rise between South America and Africa. The profile was obtained by means of a seismic recording system carried on board the Teledyne Exploration Company's research vessel *Stranger* during a west-east traverse between Trinidad, B.W.I., and Monrovia, Liberia, in June, 1967. The Teledyne "super sparker" system consists of several banks of high-voltage capacitors, which discharge into the seawater at intervals of a few seconds, generating enough steam bubbles to simulate a gaseous explosion. The resulting acoustical impulse is transmitted through the water and into the sea floor, where seismic reflections are produced by geological structures as deep as two miles below the sea floor. The reflected signals return to the surface of the ocean, where they are detected by an array of hydrophones trailed behind the ship and recorded on continuously moving paper tape. The vertical-to-horizontal-scale ratio of the resulting profile is 8:1. The segment of the profile shown on this page shows a portion of

the western abyssal plain near the base of the mid-Atlantic rise. In this region the sediments are comparatively flat and uniform; they are estimated to be from 1,000 to 1,500 meters thick. Although the basement complex underlying the sedimentary layers is quite irregular, within the sediments themselves there is little evidence of recent faulting. The water depth at this point is about 5,300 meters. At the beginning of the mid-Atlantic rise (*pages 9 to 11*) the crystalline basement structures rise abruptly above the level of the mean sea floor. In this region sediments exist only in small basins over the basement complex. As one approaches the crest of the mid-Atlantic rise (*pages 12 and 13*) there is no longer evidence of sediments even in the basins. Individual peaks and ridges rise as much as 1,700 meters above the mean sea floor near the crest. The nature of the seismic reflections in this region suggests recent as well as ancient tectonic activity. The entire section of profile reproduced on these six pages covers a distance of about 240 miles centered approximately 1,000 miles east of Trinidad. The mid-Atlantic rise is roughly 150 miles wide at this latitude.

and over the Alps in an attempt to reinforce his brother. Roman sea power countered this move by transporting 11,-000 men in ships from the Roman base in Spain back to Italy. These reinforcements, together with the Roman troops positioned between Hannibal and Hasdrubal, fell in overwhelming numbers on the younger brother at the river Metaurus. Hannibal's first news of the battle came when his brother's head was thrown into his camp. He cried out in despair that Rome would now be mistress of the world.

The importance of production in the home country for the development of sea power is shown in a negative way by the later history of Portugal. This small nation was the first in Europe to commit her fortunes to the sea and to trade with distant lands, but as Mahan writes: "The

mines of Brazil were the ruin of Portugal.... All manufactures fell into insane contempt; ere long the English supplied the Portuguese not only with clothes but with all merchandise, all commodities, even to salt, fish and grain. After their gold, the Portuguese abandoned their very soil. The vineyards of Oporto were finally bought by the English with Brazilian gold, which had only passed through Portugal to be spread throughout England. In fifty years the Brazilian mines yielded $500 million worth of gold to Portugal but at the end of that time Portugal had only $25 million left."

The Spanish galleons that plied between Mexico and the Philippines furnish a similarly negative illustration. In the annals of the conquest of the "perils and hazards of the sea" the story of these galleons is a remarkable one. Every year

for 250 years—from 1565 to 1815—the Spanish governors in Mexico sent out well-armed ships from Acapulco across the longest stretch of water in the world, carrying Mexican silver to the colony of Manila in the Philippines. There the money was exchanged for Chinese silks, porcelains, ladies' combs and other luxury goods, and the galleons laden with these commodities sailed eastward again to Mexico. Throughout the 250 years only four galleons were captured, one in 1587 by a gentleman privateer, Thomas Cavendish, and three in the 18th century during the worldwide wars in which Britain won her empire by achieving primacy at sea.

Because the trade was primarily in consumer goods and in silver, however, the Manila colony never became much more than an entrepôt for the transship-

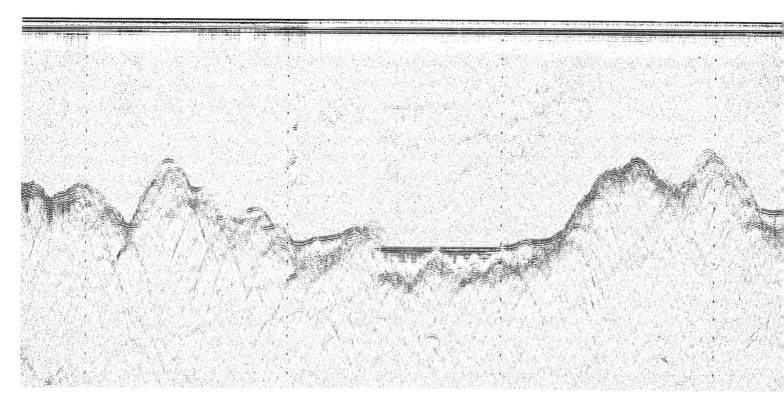

ment of Chinese luxuries. It developed no industrial or commercial life of its own, and neither Mexico nor Spain gained long-run benefits to their economies. Anglo-Saxon historians are fond of belittling the maritime skills of Spain. As the history of the Manila galleons shows, however, the Spaniards lacked neither seamanship nor naval prowess. Their failure resulted from a lack of interest and skill in manufacturing and trade.

Throughout the 17th and 18th centuries England pursued all the elements of sea power with a ruthless aggressiveness and self-confident arrogance that is hard to believe today. Even Charles II, who depended on subsidies from Louis XIV, told the Sun King when a dispute arose about the command of the combined French and English fleets against the Dutch Republic, "It is the custom of the English to command at sea." The wars of the 18th century impoverished France because of the enormous cost of her armies, while England got rich through overseas trade, supported by manufacturing at home and protected by her mastery of the seas.

In the long periods of maritime peace imposed by the supremacy of Roman and English sea power, the sea became a medium for unifying civilization. As Sir Kenneth Clark has observed, if you had visited the public square of any Mediterranean town in the first century A.D.—in Greece, Italy, France, Asia Minor or North Africa—you would hardly have known where you were, any more

than you would in a modern airport. Thus in the 18th and 19th centuries did English sea power protect the development of a new civilization around a larger ocean—the Atlantic civilization, which we are still building today.

What meaning does sea power hold for the modern world? Mahan's concepts seem outmoded in an age when superpowers can destroy each other by pushing the right buttons, when colonies have disappeared and when the North Vietnamese can laugh in the teeth of the most expensive navy the world has ever seen.

A new kind of sea power, which Mahan would scarcely recognize, now holds the center of the stage. The growing vulnerability of land-based intercontinental ballistic missiles under the impact of new weapons developments [see "Military Technology and National Security," by H. F. York; SCIENTIFIC AMERICAN, Offprint 330] makes mutual deterrence in the balance of nuclear terror hinge increasingly on the atomic-powered submarines, armed with ballistic missiles, with which the U.S.S.R. and the U.S. confront each other under the seas. In part because of the effectiveness of this deterrent, the traditional uses of sea power appear to have become obsolete.

For the foreseeable future a general war in Europe, which would require the U.S. Navy to protect vast ocean shipments of men and materials, seems the unlikeliest of possibilities. Navies, if they are to be for other purposes, will be em-

ployed only in small wars, of which unhappily there seems to be an abundance in this bitter second half of the 20th century, and to maintain the peace, wherever possible, along the coastlines of the world. These would both be major tasks but they require a radical rethinking of our inherited concepts of sea power.

The ocean first became one ocean in the consciousness of man during the age of discovery. Man's venture into the unknown was first carried past the point of no return by the Portuguese. The Infante Dom Henrique, who is called Prince Henry the Navigator by Anglo-Saxon writers, was the epitome of the spirit of this age. He made his headquarters at Sagres on Cape St. Vincent, the southwestern promontory of Europe. Here he built a kind of academy for seafaring in unknown oceans; he collected all the charts and sailing directions he could find, and he employed mathematicians and geographers to decipher them and to make new ones. The most daring and competent master mariners from Italy, Spain and Portugal entered his service. He sent them out each year farther and farther into the western ocean and down the coast of Africa. Searching for the mythical Isles of St. Brendan (a seagoing Irish saint whose largely imaginary sea stories were popular throughout the Middle Ages), his captains found the Azores.

Prince Henry's great objective, however, was to send his ships down the coast of Africa beyond Cape Bojador,

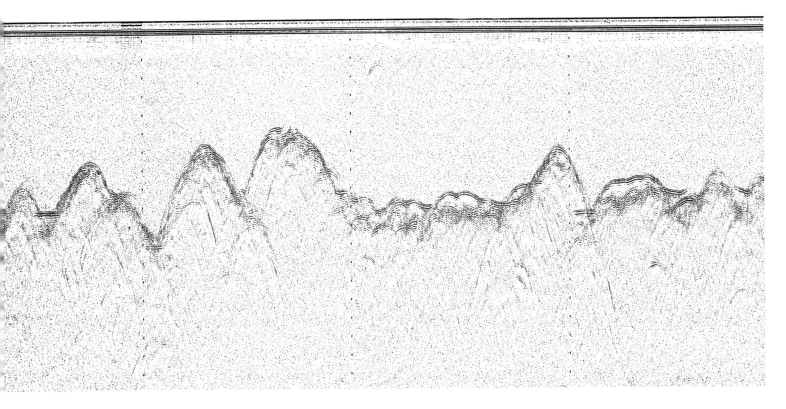

and if possible around the southern point of that continent on a new route to the Indies. This was a fearful challenge. Beyond the cape, according to ancient lore, lay the impassable Tropical Zone, with water temperatures that reached the boiling point at the Equator. Equally serious was the undoubted fact that both the wind and the current were dead ahead whenever the Portuguese caravels tried to lay a course for their return voyage home. Cape Bojador was finally rounded in 1434, and by the year of Prince Henry's death (1460) the Portuguese had reached within 10 degrees of the Equator. Then they swept rapidly onward; only 28 years later Bartholomeu Diaz sailed to the southernmost point of Africa, which he called the Cape of Storms. The Portuguese king renamed it the Cape of Good Hope, in joyful anticipation of Vasco da Gama's shortly to be accomplished voyage to Calicut.

For 100 years after Prince Henry's death Portugal, which was called Lusitania by the Romans, merited Camoëns' splendid boast in the "Lusiads," the epic poem that celebrates Vasco da Gama's expedition:

Behold her seated here, both head and
    key
Of Europe all, the Lusitanian queen;
Where endeth land and where beginneth
    sea;
Where Phoebus goeth down in ocean
    green.

The path had been laid to the treasures of the East and to an empire whose bedraggled and unhappy remnants still exist.

Prince Henry compels our admiration for his vision and leadership. His world of faith and terrors was so different from our own, however, that we have difficulty visualizing it. In contrast Captain James Cook is almost a contemporary. He would have felt at home on a modern oceanographic expedition into the deep Pacific and would have approved its objectives.

Cook's journals are models of modest and clear writing. Like all good marine surveyors he also made painstakingly accurate sketches and maps of the islands and shorelines he visited. He had the eye of an artist, seeing many things other men did not see, and the curiosity and powers of logical thought of a scientist.

Of Cook's two great discoveries, one was negative. This was the nonexistence of Terra Australis, a huge imaginary continent that for hundreds of years had been thought to cut off the Southern Ocean beyond about 50 degrees south latitude. Between 1768 and 1775 Cook twice sailed around the world in his small ships Endeavour, Resolution and Adventure, crisscrossing many times the "roaring forties" and the "howling fifties" and finding no land. He noticed, however, that the icebergs he encountered near the southern limits of his track were free of salt. He deduced that they must have broken off from huge glaciers on a land mass beyond the Antarctic Circle.

In these high southern latitudes Cook also noted the presence of numerous albatrosses and stormy petrels. This seemed independent proof of a large land mass to the south, where these birds could nest. Thus in his mind's eye Cook saw Antarctica, although that continent was not actually discovered for another 50 years.

Cook's discovery of the Hawaiian Islands, the largest of the Polynesians and the islands farthest from any continent, was an accident. Cook found them on his way to Alaska and the Arctic Ocean in search of a northwest passage between Europe and Asia. He was as astonished as we are today that the Spanish Manila galleons had never found them.

It has been said that Cook's epitaph is the map of the Pacific, almost as we now know it. If you are planning a cruise to the South Sea Islands, many of the charts you will obtain from the Naval Oceanographic Office will bear this notation: "From an Admiralty Survey in 1769" (or some other date from 1768 to 1777). The survey was made by Cook.

Cook mapped Palmerston Atoll, a lonely speck halfway between Samoa and Tahiti in the archipelago named after him, in 1774. He made a note of strong currents around the atoll. On the Capricorn Expedition of the Scripps Institution of Oceanography we had the great satisfaction of proving that he had made one of his rare mistakes. Without benefit of echo-sounding gear, Cook had evidently become confused in his sextant

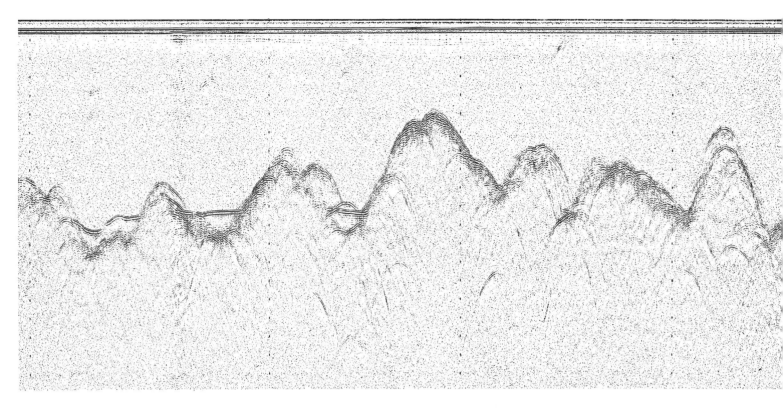

fixes on the low, almost indistinguishable landmarks around the atoll. As a result his survey had failed to close by about two miles. He concluded that this was due to currents that retarded the ship. Actually the atoll is two miles longer than he thought it was, and the currents do not exist.

From a scientific point of view there are many properties of the oceans and of seawater that combine to determine the relationships between man and the sea. The most obvious are the oceans' vast area, great depth and huge volume. Seawater is the most abundant substance accessible to man, and all the continents are islands in the midst of the world-girdling sea. The periphery, or shoreline, of the oceans is several times longer than it would need to be if the waters were contained in a simple circular basin. This long shoreline gives many peoples access to the sea and enables them to enjoy its benefits. More important, the shoreline allows relatively easy access to vast areas of the land. In the words of Mahan, "the powers ruling the sea are always near any country whose ports are open to their ships."

Because of the complex shape of the boundaries between the land and the sea, certain small parts of the oceans have an importance that far outweighs their area. These are the narrow seas, the straits and passages between the land that lie athwart the well-traveled trade routes of nations. They are the best-known places in the sea, as is easily seen by reciting some of their names: Bosporus and Dardanelles, Kattegat and Skagerrak, Gibraltar and Bab el Mandeb, Florida and Torres, Tsushima and Malacca, the St. George Channel and the Strait of Dover. To these must be added the narrow isthmuses that join the continents, Panama and Suez.

The fluid character of water on our planet is the miracle that makes life possible, but it also means that the oceans fill all the low places of the earth. Because of this geographical fact the oceans are the ultimate receptacle of the wastes of the land, including the wastes that are produced in ever increasing amounts by human beings and their industries.

The relatively high density and low viscosity of seawater are the essential qualities that make the sea surface a broad and easily traveled highway. In technical terms the water provides a high lift-drag ratio to the ships that float on it; consequently large ships and heavy cargoes can be moved fairly rapidly across the ocean with comparatively little motive power. Maritime commerce would be impossible if seawater were as viscous as molasses, and the fuel required to carry the huge cargoes of modern ships would be prohibitively expensive if the water were as light as air. At the same time the combination of low viscosity and high density gives rise to the principal hazard of the sea, the giant wind-waves caused by storms that crush small ships and fiercely attack coastal structures. If the water were much more viscous, the wind could not build up high, steep waves, and if it were much lighter, the wave force would be insignificant.

The high surface tension of seawater, although not of fundamental importance, is a matter of considerable convenience to human beings because it means that the water does not stick to surfaces with which it comes in contact but runs off easily and leaves them relatively dry. Seagoing would be a messy business if the oceans consisted of oil. The high density and fluidity of the water create a serious difficulty when men attempt to lower themselves or their equipment deep below the surface: the enormous hydrostatic pressure at great depths, which crushes all but the strongest vessels, forms air pockets in submarine cables and produces high stresses in equipment made of materials with different compressibilities.

From the human standpoint the saltiness of seawater is its most undesirable quality. Because of its high salt content men can neither drink it nor use it to water their crops. The ionized salts make the water a good conductor of electricity, with the result that the ocean can be penetrated for only a short distance by radio waves, and electrolytic reactions between dissimilar metals or compounds proceed very rapidly. The salts plus dissolved oxygen cause seawater to be a highly corrosive substance for most man-made objects. When immersed in the sea, the works of man soon suffer a sea change into something that may be rich

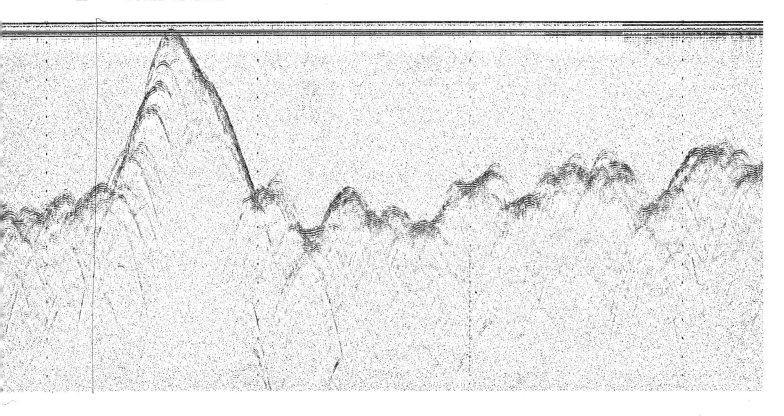

and strange but is usually useless for human purposes. This quality of seawater makes research in materials a strategic salient in the progress of ocean technology [see "Technology and the Ocean," by Willard Bascom, page 107].

Seawater is much less transparent to visible light than air is, but it is more transparent than most other substances. This intermediate transparency, combined with a high heat capacity and a high heat of vaporization, makes the ocean the regulator in the great thermal engine of the ocean and the atmosphere [see "The Atmosphere and the Ocean," by R. W. Stewart, page 27]. Most of the energy of sunlight passes virtually unimpeded throughout the atmosphere into the ocean, where it is absorbed and transformed. Nearly a third of all solar energy reaching the earth's surface goes to evaporate seawater. The thermal inertia of the sea, the circulation of the water and the geographic distribution of ocean and land profoundly influence our planet's weather and climate.

The moderate transparency and high density of seawater, and the great depth of the ocean, give life in the sea a very different character from that on land [see "The Nature of Oceanic Life," by John D. Isaacs, page 65]. Photosynthesis can take place only in the waters near the surface where bright sunlight penetrates, and consequently marine plants in the open ocean cannot support themselves on solid ground. Most marine plants have solved this problem by

being extremely small, so that they have a large surface-to-volume ratio and sink or rise slowly through the water. To maintain their small size they have a short life-span, measured in hours or days rather than in the seasons or centuries that characterize land plants. Consequently, although the total production of organic matter in the most fertile regions of the ocean is higher than that in fertile land areas, the biomass of marine plants at any one time is small.

The animals of the sea have been forced to adjust themselves to this regime of the plants, with the result that the food web in the sea is much more complex than on land, and the animals that can be utilized by man make up only a small part of the organic production of the ocean. The plants themselves are present in such low concentration that they cannot be economically harvested. The potential harvest of human food from the sea is still far from being realized by human beings. Yet, as S. J. Holt shows [see "The Food Resources of the Ocean," page 93], it will never be possible for men to obtain more than a fraction of their food requirements from the ocean.

From the biologist's point of view one of the most important characteristics of the ocean is its great age, even on a geologic time scale. Time has been available for the evolution of many different forms of life. As a result living things in the sea present an incredible diversity. Some 200,000 species have already been identified and new ones are found on every

oceanographic expedition. Some of these are "living fossils" from the ancient past and others have evolved recently.

In former times men were chiefly concerned with the surface of the sea, together with the near-surface waters and shallow seabed that were accessible to fishermen. As our technology advances, however, our ability to penetrate and use the entire huge volume of the ocean and to explore and exploit the seabed, even to the greatest depths, is rapidly increasing. The shape of the sea floor, the properties of the deep waters and the distribution of deep-sea resources have thus become of much greater interest than previously. As K. O. Emery and Edward Wenk, Jr., set forth at greater length [see "The Continental Shelves," page 39, and "The Physical Resources of the Ocean," page 81], the margins of the oceans surrounding the continents, containing the continental shelves and slopes and the deeper continental rise, are probably the principal location for the most important mineral resources underneath the sea: petroleum and natural gas. The living resources seem to exist almost entirely in the upper 1,500 meters, and like the fossil fuels they are most concentrated over the continental shelves and slopes.

Submarine vehicles for both military and peaceful purposes are a spectacular element of the new marine technology. From a military point of view the great advantage of submarines rests on the low transparency of seawater for visible light and radio waves. A deeply sub-

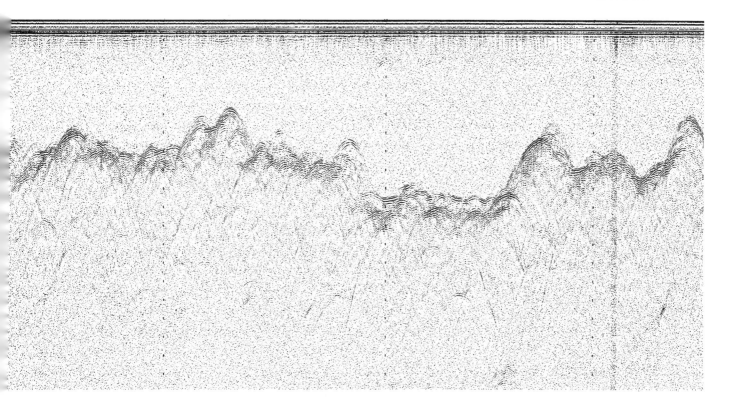

merged submarine can neither be seen visually nor be detected by radar. The submarine itself would be equally blind were it not for one of the most remarkable qualities of the ocean: its capacity to transmit low-frequency sounds over great distances.

The explosion of a one-pound block of dynamite in the air can be heard for about half a mile. Such an explosion at mid-depths in the ocean can be heard for many thousands of miles. The ocean is far from being a perfect acoustical transmitter, however. It is full of background noises made by animals and volcanoes; the surface and the bottom scatter and absorb sound; variations in temperature and density bend and distort sound waves in complicated ways, and the ocean rings with echoes like a badly designed auditorium. To elucidate and overcome these imperfections in sound propagation is one of the major problems of marine technology.

We may confidently expect that the ocean will be far more important to mankind in the future than it has ever been in the past. Recognition of the new opportunities in the ocean has brought a widening realization that the organization of human society into national states, which works, however imperfectly, on the land, is not well suited to the optimum utilization of the sea. A new kind of regime is needed in which the interests of all states are protected but those of humanity as a whole are paramount. The possible nature of such a regime is now being widely discussed in the United Nations and other international forums. It is too early to forecast what may emerge. Nevertheless, it can be hoped that agreement will be reached on a set of principles somewhat as follows:

1. The resources of the high seas and the underlying seabed, outside those areas adjacent to the coasts in which the coastal states exercise certain exclusive rights, are the common heritage of mankind and shall be used and conserved in the common interest of all men. All countries shall participate in an equitable manner in the benefits gained from these resources. Individual states shall not appropriate any part of the high seas or of the underlying seabed.

2. The areas adjacent to the coasts in which coastal states exercise certain exclusive rights shall be as small as feasible, and the outer limits of these areas shall be fixed by a definite depth or distance from shore or by a formula involving both depth and distance. This outer boundary, together with the nature of the exclusive rights to be exercised, should be determined by international agreement as soon as possible.

3. Internationally coordinated action must be taken to prevent pollution of the ocean, including control of pollutants coming from the land or the air, such as pesticides, radioactive substances, poisonous chemicals and sewage; from ships, submarines or other equipment used at sea, and from exploitation of marine resources, for example exploration, production, storage and transportation of oil and gas.

4. The freedom of scientific research in the ocean shall be kept inviolate. The exclusive rights granted to the coastal states shall not include the right to interfere with scientific research, provided that the coastal state is given prior notification of the plan to conduct the research, has full opportunity to participate in it and has access to all the data obtained and samples collected, and provided that the research does not deleteriously affect marine resources or other uses of the sea.

5. Greatly intensified international cooperation and coordination in all peaceful uses of the ocean is needed to encourage and advance beneficial exploitation of marine resources and technological developments for this purpose, to ensure the conservation and rational use of resources, and to minimize interference among uses of different resources and among different uses of the same resource.

6. The military uses of the ocean floor shall be as limited as practicable; in particular, no nuclear weapons shall be planted on it.

Agreement on these principles and on creation of an international regime to secure them depends largely, although by no means entirely, on the U.S. It is to be hoped that our government and people will be farsighted enough to see that their own long-range interests lie in a generous approach to the new age of the oceans.

II

The Origin of the Oceans

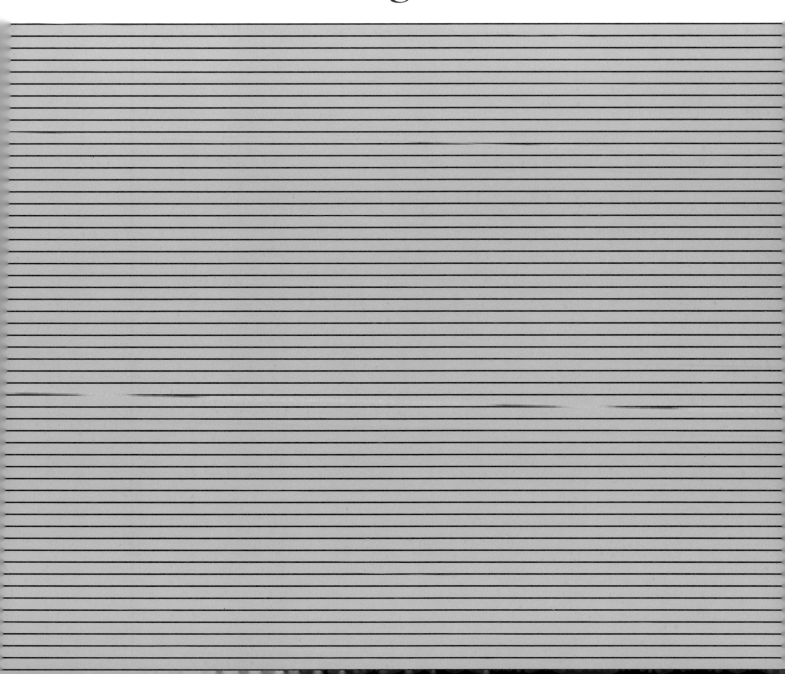

The Origin of the Oceans

SIR EDWARD BULLARD

*In recent years it has become increasingly apparent that
the floor of the deep ocean is remarkably young.
It is growing outward from mid-ocean ridges, pushing
most of the continents apart as it does*

The earth is uniquely favored among the planets: it has rain, rivers and seas. The large planets (Jupiter, Saturn, Uranus and Neptune) have only a small solid core, presumably overlain by gases liquefied by pressure; they are also surrounded by enormous atmospheres. The inner planets are more like the earth. Mercury, however, has practically no atmosphere and the side of the planet facing the sun is hot enough to melt lead. Venus has a thick atmosphere containing little water and a surface that, according to recent measurements, may be even hotter than the surface of Mercury. Mars and the moon appear to show us their primeval surfaces, affected only by craters formed by the impact of meteorites, and perhaps by volcanoes. Only on the earth has the repetition of erosion and sedimentation —"the colossal hour glass of rock destruction and rock formation"—run its course cycle after cycle and produced the diverse surface that we see. The mountains are raised and then worn away by falling and running water; the debris is carried onto the lowlands and then out to the ocean. Geologically speaking, the process is rapid. The great plateau of Africa is reduced by a foot in a few thousand years, and in a few million years it will be near sea level, like the Precambrian rocks of Canada and Finland. All trace of the original surface of the earth has been removed, but as far back as one can see there is evidence in rounded, water-worn pebbles for the existence of running water and therefore, presumably, of an ocean and of dry land.

The obvious things that no one comments on are often the most remarkable; one of them is the constancy of the total volume of water through the ages. The level of the sea, of course, has varied from time to time. During the ice ages,

when much water was locked up in ice sheets on the continents, the level of the sea was lower than it is at present, and the continental shelves of Europe and North America were laid bare. Often the sea has advanced over the coastal plains, but never has it covered all the land or even most of it. The mechanism of this equilibrium is unknown; it might have been expected that water would be expelled gradually from the interior of the earth and that the seas would grow steadily larger, or that water would be dissociated into hydrogen and oxygen in the upper atmosphere and that the hydrogen would escape, leading to a gradual drying up of the seas. These things either do not happen or they balance each other.

The mystery is deepened by the almost complete loss of neon from the earth; in the sun and the stars neon is only a little rarer than oxygen. The neon was presumably lost when the earth was built up from dust and solid grains because neon normally does not form compounds, but if that is so, why was the water not lost too? Water has a molecular weight of 18, which is less than the atomic weight of neon, and thus should escape more easily. It looks as if the water must have been tied up in compounds, perhaps hydrated silicates, until the earth had formed and the neon had escaped. Water must then have been released as a liquid sometime during the first billion years of the earth's history, for which we have no geological record. The planet Mercury and the moon would have been too small to retain water after it was released. Mars seems to have been able to retain a trace, not enough to make oceans but enough to be detectable by spectroscopy.

These speculations about the early history of the earth are open to many doubts. The evidence is almost non-existent, and all one can say is, "It might have been that. . . ." The great increase in understanding of the present state and recent history of the ocean basins that we have gained in the past 20 years is something quite different. For the first time the geology of the oceans has been studied with energy and resources commensurate with the tremendous task. It turns out that the main processes of geology can be understood only when the oceans have been studied; no amount of effort on land could have told us what we now know. The study of marine geology has unlocked the history of the oceans, and it seems likely to make intelligible the history of the continents as well. We are in the middle of a rejuvenating process in geology comparable to the one that physics experienced in the 1890's and to the one that is now in progress in molecular biology.

The critical step was the realization that the oceans are quite different from the continents. The mountains of the oceans are nothing like the Alps or the Rockies, which are largely built from folded sediments. There is a world-encircling mountain range—the mid-ocean ridge—on the sea bottom, but it is built entirely of igneous rocks, of basalts that have emerged from the interior of the earth. Although the undersea mountains have a covering of sediments in

RED SEA and the Gulf of Aden represent two of the newest seaways created by the worldwide spreading of the ocean floor. In this photograph, taken at an altitude of 390 miles from the spacecraft *Gemini 11* in September, 1966, the Red Sea separates Ethiopia (*at left*) from the Arabian peninsula (*at right*). The Gulf of Aden lies between the southern shore of Arabia and Somalia. The excellent fit between the drifting land masses is depicted in the illustrations on page 19.

16

many places, they are not made of sediments, they are not folded and they have not been compressed.

A cracklike valley runs along the crest of the mid-ocean ridge for most of its length, and it is here that new ocean floor is being formed today [*see illustration on next two pages*]. From a study of the numerous earthquakes along this crack it is clear that the two sides are moving apart and that the crack would continually widen if it were not being filled with material from below. As the rocks on the two sides move away and new rock solidifies in the crack, the events are recorded by a kind of geological tape recorder: the newly solidified rock is magnetized in the direction of the earth's magnetic field. For at least the past 10,000 years, and possibly for as long as 700,000 years, the north magnetic pole has been close to its present location, so that the magnetic field is to the north and downward in the Northern Hemisphere, and to the north and upward in the Southern Hemisphere. As the cracking and the spreading of the ocean floor go on, a strip of magnetized rock is produced. Then one day, or rather in the course of several thousand years, the earth's field reverses, the next effusion of lava is magnetized in the reverse direction and a strip of reversely magnetized rocks is built up between the two split halves of the earlier strip. The reversals succeed one another at widely varying intervals; sometimes the change comes after 50,000 years, often there is no change for a million years and occasionally, as during the Permian period, there is no reversal for 20 million years. The sequence of reversals and the progress of spreading is recorded in all the oceans by the magnetization of the rocks of the ocean floor. The message can be read by a magnetometer towed behind a ship.

We now have enough examples of these magnetic messages to leave no doubt about what is happening. It is a

PROBABLE ARRANGEMENT of continents before the formation of the Atlantic Ocean was determined by the author with the aid of a computer. The fit was made not at the present coastlines but at the true edge of each continent, the line where the continental shelf (*dark brown*) slopes down steeply to the sea floor. Overlapping land and shelf areas are reddish orange; gaps where the continental edges do not quite meet are dark blue. At present the entire western Atlantic is moving as one great plate carrying both North America and South America with it. At an earlier period the two continents must have moved independently.

truly remarkable fact that the results of magnetic surveys in the South Pacific can be explained—indeed predicted—from the sequence of reversals of the direction of the earth's magnetic field known from magnetic and age measurements, made quite independently on lavas in California, Africa and elsewhere. The only adjustable factor in the calculation is the rate of spreading. Such worldwide theoretical ideas and such detailed agreement between calculation and theory are rare in geology, where theories are usually qualitative, local and of little predictive value.

The speed of spreading on each side of a mid-ocean ridge varies from less than a centimeter per year to as much as eight centimeters. The fastest rate is the one from the East Pacific Rise and the slowest rates are those from the Mid-Atlantic Ridge and from the Carlsberg Ridge of the northwest Indian Ocean. The rate of production of new terrestrial crust at the central valley of a ridge is the sum of the rates of spreading on the two sides. Since the rates on the two sides are commonly almost equal, this sum is twice the rate on each side and may be as much as 16 centimeters (six inches) per year. Such rates are, geologically speaking, fast. At 16 centimeters per year the entire floor of the Pacific Ocean, which is about 15,000 kilometers (10,000 miles) wide, could be produced in 100 million years.

When the mid-ocean ridges are examined in more detail, they are found not to be continuous but to be cut into sections by "fracture zones" [*see top illustration on page 22*]. A study of the earthquakes on these fracture zones shows that the separate pieces of ridge crest on the two sides of a fracture zone are not moving apart, as might seem likely on first consideration. The two pieces of ridge remain fixed with respect to each other while on each side a plate of the crust moves away as a rigid body; such a fracture is called a transform fault. The earthquakes occur only on the piece of the fracture zone between the two ridge crests; there is no relative motion along the parts outside this section.

If two rigid plates on a sphere are spreading out on each side of a ridge that is crossed by fracture zones, the relative motion of the two plates must be a rotation around some point, termed the pole of spreading. The "axis of spreading," around which the rotation takes place, passes through this pole and the center of the earth. The existence of a pole of spreading and an axis of spreading is geometrically necessary, as was shown by Leonhard Euler in the

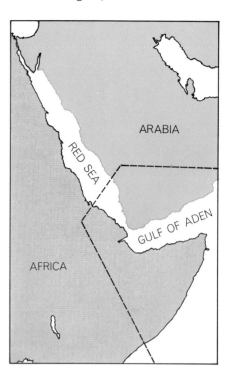

RUPTURE OF MIDDLE EAST is being caused by the widening of the Red Sea and the Gulf of Aden. Some 20 million years ago the Arabian peninsula was joined to Africa, as evidenced by the remarkable fit between shorelines (*see illustration below*). The area within the *Gemini 11* photograph on page 17 is shown by the broken lines.

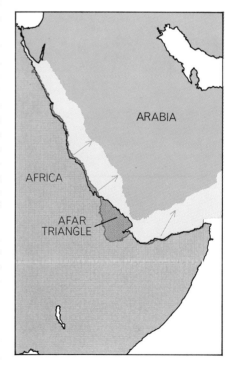

FIT OF SHORELINES of Arabia and Africa works out most successfully if the African coast (*black*) is left intact and if the Arabian coast (*color*) is superposed in two separate sections. In the reconstruction a corner of Arabia overlaps the "Afar triangle" in northern Ethiopia, an area that now has some of the characteristics of an ocean floor.

18th century. If the only motion on the fracture zones is the sliding of the two plates past each other, then the fracture zones must lie along circles of latitude with respect to the pole of spreading, and the rates of spreading at any point on the ridge must be proportional to the perpendicular distance from the point to the axis of spreading [*see bottom illustration on page 22*].

All of this is well verified for the spreading that is going on today. The rates of spreading can be obtained from the magnetic patterns and the dates of the reversals. The poles of spreading can be found from the directions of the fracture zones and checked by the direction of earthquake motions. It turns out that the ridge axes and the magnetic pattern are usually almost at right angles to the fracture zones. This is not a geometrical

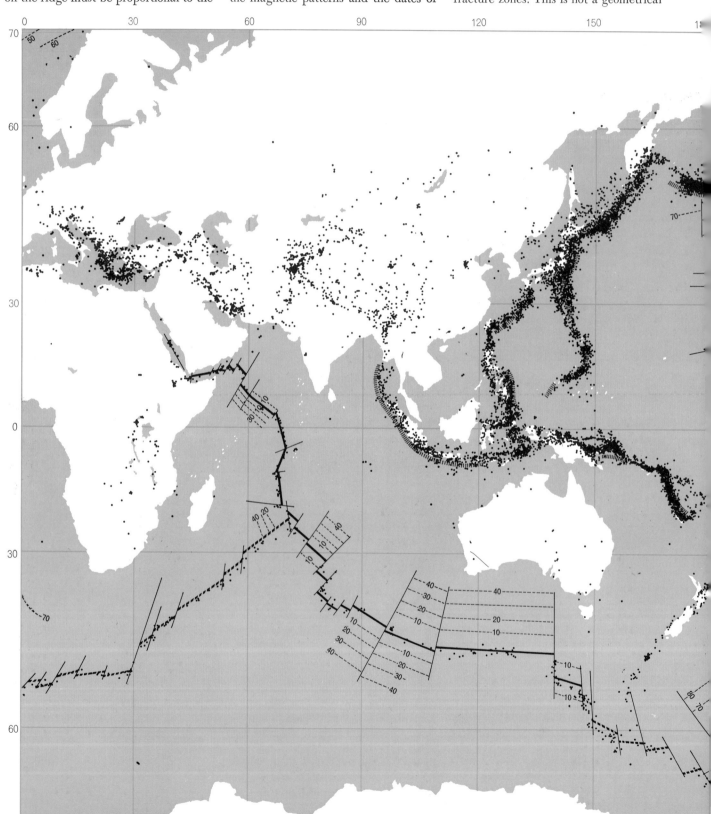

OCEANIC GEOLOGY has turned out to be much simpler than the geology of the continents. New ocean bottom is continuously being extruded along the crest of a worldwide system of ridges (*thick black lines*). The present position of material extruded at intervals of 10 million years, as determined by magnetic studies, appears as broken lines parallel to the ridge system, which is offset by fracture

necessity, but when it does happen it means that the lines of the ridge axes and of the magnetic pattern must, if they are extrapolated, go through the pole of spreading. If the ridge consists of a number of offset sections at right angles to the fracture zones, the axes of these sections will converge on the pole of spreading. It is one of the surprises of the work at sea that this rather simple geometry embraces so large a part of the facts. It seems that marine geology is truly simpler than continental geology and that this is not merely an illusion based on our lesser knowledge of the oceans.

The regularity of the magnetic pattern suggests that the ocean floor can move as a rigid plate over areas several thousand kilometers across. The thickness of the rigid moving plate is quite uncertain,

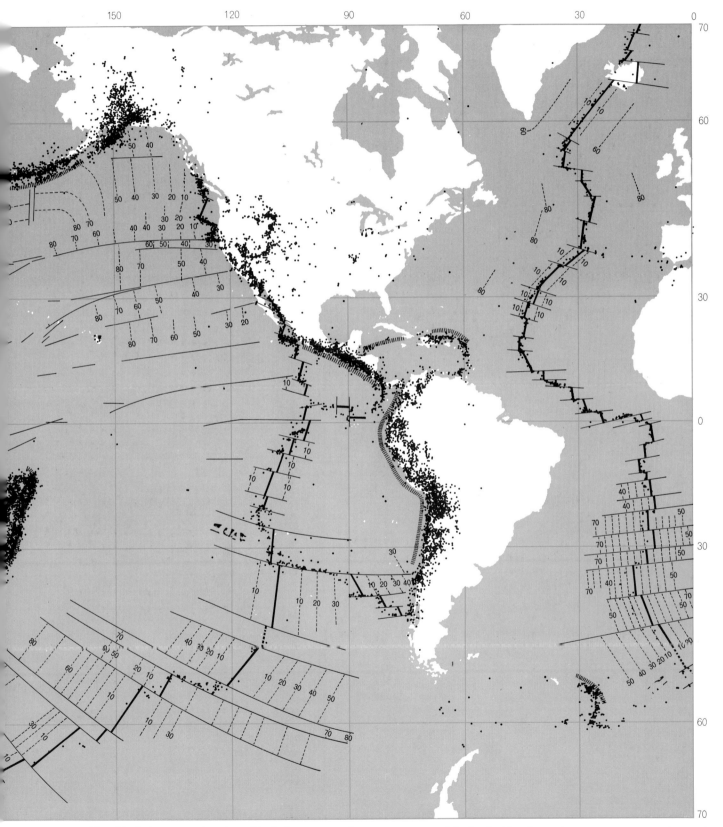

zones (*thin black lines*). Earthquakes (*black dots*) occur along the crests of ridges, on parts of the fracture zone and along deep trenches. These trenches, where the ocean floor dips steeply, are represented by hatched bands. At the maximum estimated rate of sea-floor spreading, about 16 centimeters a year, the entire floor of the Pacific Ocean could be created in perhaps 100 million years.

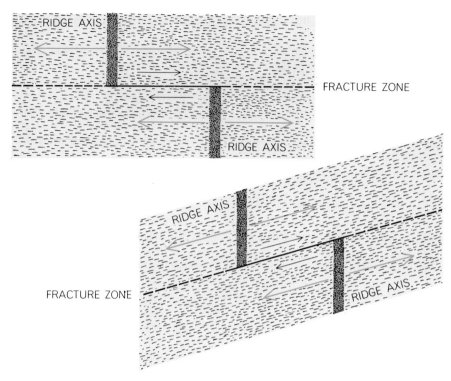

MOTION AT AXIS OF RIDGE consists of an opening of an axial crack (*vertical bands*) where two plates separate (*arrows*). Often the ridge is offset by a fracture zone, making a transform fault where one plate slips past another. The motion must be parallel to the fracture zone. It is usually at right angles to the ridge (*upper left*) but need not be (*lower right*).

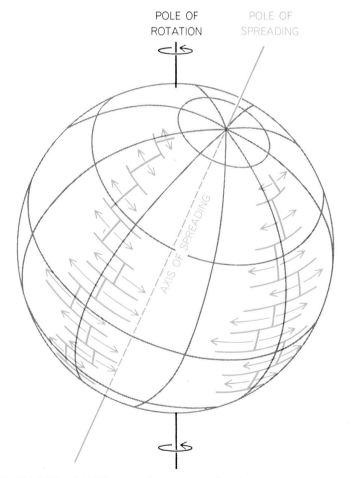

MOTION OF RIGID PLATES on a sphere requires that the plates rotate around a "pole of spreading" through which passes an "axis of spreading." Plates always move parallel to the fracture zones and along circles of latitude perpendicular to the axis of spreading. The rate of spreading is slowest near the pole of spreading and fastest 90 degrees away from it. The spreading pole can be quite remote from the sphere's pole of rotation.

but a value between 70 and 100 kilometers seems likely. If this is so, the greater part of the plate will be made of the same material as the upper part of the earth's mantle—probably of peridotite, a rock largely composed of olivine, a silicate of magnesium and iron, $(Mg, Fe)_2SiO_4$. The basaltic rocks of the oceanic crust will form the upper five kilometers or so of the plate, with a veneer of sediments on top.

What happens at the boundary of an ocean and a continent? Sometimes, as in the South Atlantic, nothing happens; there are no earthquakes, no distortion, nothing to indicate relative motion between the sea floor and the bordering continent. The continent can then be regarded as part of the same plate as the adjacent ocean floor; the rocks of the continental crust evidently ride on top of the plate and move with it. In other places there is another kind of coast, what Eduard Suess called "a Pacific coast." Such a coast is typified by the Pacific coast of South America. Here the oceanic plate dives under the continent and goes down at an angle of about 45 degrees. On the upper surface of this sloping plate there are numerous earthquakes—quite shallow ones near the coast and others as deep as 700 kilometers inland, under the continent. The evidence for the sinking plate has been beautifully confirmed by the discovery that seismic waves from shallow earthquakes and explosions, occurring near the place where the plate starts its dive, travel faster down the plate than they do in other directions. This is expected because the plate is relatively cold, whereas the upper mantle, into which the plate is sinking, is made of similar material but is hot.

Little is known of the detailed behavior of the plate; further study is vital for an understanding of the phenomena along the edges of continents. Near the point where the plate turns down there is an ocean deep, whose mode of formation is not precisely understood, but if a plate goes down, it is not difficult to imagine ways in which it could leave a depression in the sea floor. It is probable that, as the plate goes down, some of the sediment on its surface is scraped off and piled up in a jumbled mass on the landward side of the ocean deep. This sediment may later be incorporated in the mountain range that usually appears on the edge of the continent. The mountain range bordering the continent commonly has a row of volcanoes, as in the Andes. The lavas from the volcanoes are frequently composed of andesites, which are different from the lavas of the mid-ocean ridges in that they contain more silica. It may reasonably be supposed that they are formed by the partial melting of the descending plate at a depth of about 150 kilometers. The first material to melt will contain more silica than the remaining material; it is also possible that the melted material is contaminated by granite as it rises to the surface through the continental rocks.

In many places the sinking plate goes down under a chain of islands and not under the continent itself. This happens in the Aleutians, to the south of Indonesia, off the islands of the Tonga group, in the Caribbean and in many other places. The volcanoes are then on the islands and the deep earthquakes occur under the almost enclosed sea behind the chain or arc of islands, as they do in the Sea of Japan, the Sea of Okhotsk and the Java Sea.

The destruction of oceanic crust explains one of the great paradoxes of geology. There have always been oceans, but the present oceans contain no sediment more than 150 million years old and very little sediment older than 80 million years. The explanation is that the older sediments have been carried away with the plates and are either piled up at the edge of a continent or are carried down with a sinking plate and lost in the mantle.

The picture is simple: the greater part of the earth's surface is divided into six plates [*see illustration on next two pages*]. These plates move as rigid bodies, new material for them being produced from the upper mantle by lava emerging from the crack along the crest of a mid-ocean ridge. Plates are destroyed at the oceanic trenches by plunging into the mantle, where ultimately they are mixed again with the material whence they came. The scheme is not yet established in all its details. Perhaps the greatest uncertainty is in the section of the ridge running south of South Africa; it is not clear how much of this is truly a ridge and a source of new crust and how much is a series of transform faults with only tangential motion. It is also uncertain whether the American and Eurasian plates meet in Alaska or in Siberia. It appears certain, however, that they do not meet along the Bering Strait.

A close look at the system of ridges, fracture zones, trenches and earthquakes reveals many other features of great interest, which can only be mentioned here. The Red Sea and the Gulf of Aden appear to be embryo oceans [*see illustration on page 17*]. Their floors are truly oceanic, with no continental

rocks; along their axes one can find offset lengths of crack joined by fracture zones, and magnetic surveys show the worldwide magnetic pattern but only the most recent parts of it. These seas are being formed by the movement of Africa and Arabia away from each other. A detailed study of the geology, the topography and the present motion suggests that the separation started 20 million years ago in the Miocene period and that it is still continuing. If this is so, there must have been a sliding movement along the Jordan rift valley, with the area to the east having moved about 100 kilometers northward with respect to the western portion. There must also have been an opening of the East African rift valley by 65 kilometers or so.

The first of these displacements is well established by geological comparisons between the two sides of the valley, and it should be possible to verify the second. The reassembly of the pieces requires that the southwest corner of Arabia overlap the "Afar triangle" ·in northern Ethiopia [*see bottom illustration on page 19*]. This area should therefore be part of the embryo ocean. The fact that it is dry land presented a substantial puzzle, but recently it has been shown that the oceanic magnetic pattern extends over the area; it is the only land area in the world where this is known to happen. It seems likely that the Afar triangle is in some sense oceanic. The results of gravity surveys, seismic measurements and drilling will be awaited with interest. On this picture Arabia and the area to the north comprise a small plate separate from the African and Asian plates. The northern boundary of this small plate may be in the mountains of Iran and Turkey, where motion is proceeding today.

A number of other small plates are known. There is one between the Pacific coast of Canada and the ridge off Vancouver Island; it is probable that this is being crumpled at the coast rather than diving under the continent. Farther south the plate and the ridge from which it spread may have been overrun by the westward motion of North America. The ridge appears again in the Gulf of California, which is similar in many ways to the Red Sea and the Gulf of Aden. From the mouth of the Gulf of California the ridge runs southward and is joined by an east-west ridge running through the Galápagos Islands. The sea floor bounded by the two ridges and the trench off Central America seems to constitute a separate small plate.

For the past four million years we can date the lavas on land with enough

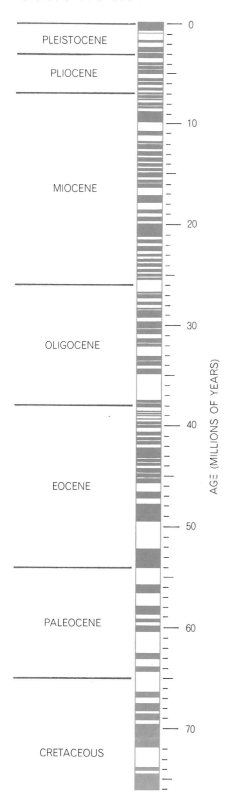

REVERSALS of the earth's magnetic field can be traced back more than 70 million years using magnetic patterns observed on the sea floor. The timetable of reversals for the most recent four million years was obtained by dating reversals in lava flows on land. Extrapolations beyond that assume that the sea floor spread at a constant rate. Colored bars show periods when the direction of the magnetic field was as it is now.

accuracy to give a timetable of magnetic reversals that can be correlated with the magnetic pattern on the sea bottom. For this period the rates of spreading from the ridges have remained constant. Further back we have a long series of reversals recorded in the ocean floor, but we cannot date them by comparison with lavas on land because the accuracy of the dates is insufficient to put the lavas in order. A rough guess can be made of the time since the oldest part of the magnetic pattern was formed by assuming that the rates have always been what they are today. This yields about 70 million years in the eastern Pacific and the South Atlantic. In fact the spacings of the older magnetic lineations are not in a constant proportion in the different oceans. The rates of spreading must therefore vary with time when long periods are considered. Directions of motion have also changed during this

period, as can be seen from the departure of the older parts of some of the Pacific fracture zones from circles of latitude around the present pole of spreading. A change of direction is also shown by the accurate geometrical and geochronological fit that can be made between South America and Africa [see illustration on page 18]. A rotation around the present pole of spreading will not bring the continents together; it is therefore likely that in the early stages of the separation motion was around a point farther to the south.

The ideas of the development of the earth's surface by plate formation, plate motion and plate destruction can be checked with some rigor by drilling. If they are correct, drilling at any point should show sediments of all ages from the present to the time at which this part of the plate was in the central valley of

the ridge. Under these sediments there should be lavas of about the same age as the lowest sediments. From preliminary reports of the drilling by the JOIDES project (a joint enterprise of five American universities) it seems that this expectation has been brilliantly verified and that the rate of spreading has been roughly constant for 70 million years in the South Atlantic. Such studies are of great importance because they will give firm dates for the entire magnetic pattern and provide a detailed chronology for all parts of the ocean floor.

The process of consumption of oceanic crust at the edge of a continent may proceed for tens of millions of years, but if the plate that is being consumed carries a continental fragment, then the consumption must stop when the fragment reaches the trench and collides with the continent beyond it. Because

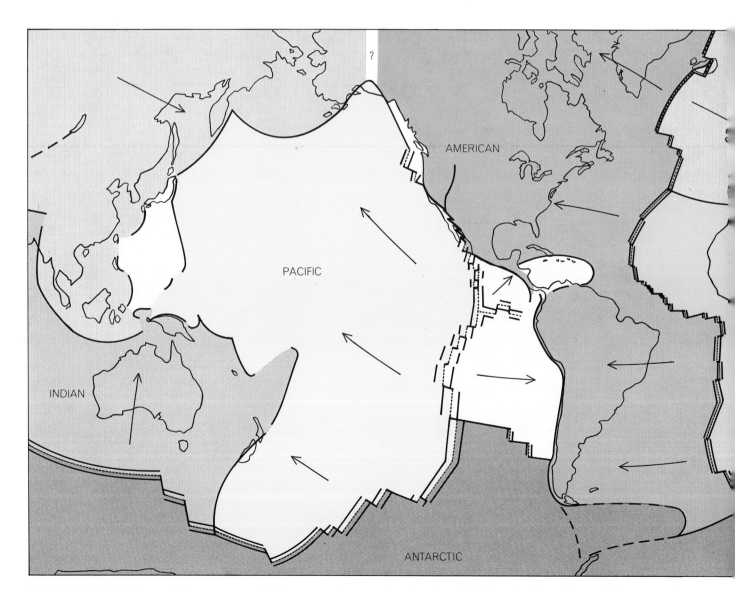

SIX MAJOR PLATES are sufficient to account for the pattern of continental drift inferred to be taking place today. In this model the African plate is assumed to be stationary. Arrows show the direction of motion of the five other large plates, which are generally bounded by ridges or trenches. Several smaller plates, unnamed, also appear. In certain areas, particularly at the junction of

the fragment consists of relatively light rocks it cannot be forced under a continent. The clearest example is the collision of India with what was once the southern margin of Asia. Paleomagnetic work shows that India has been moving northward for the past 100 million years. If it is attached to the plate that is spreading northward and eastward from the Carlsberg Ridge (which runs down the Indian Ocean halfway between Africa and India), then the motion is continuing today. This motion may be the cause of the earthquakes of the Himalayas, and it may also be connected with the formation of the mountains and of the deep sediment-filled trough to the south of them. The exact place where the joint occurs is far from clear and needs study by those with a detailed geological knowledge of northern India.

It seems unlikely that all the continents were collected in a single block for

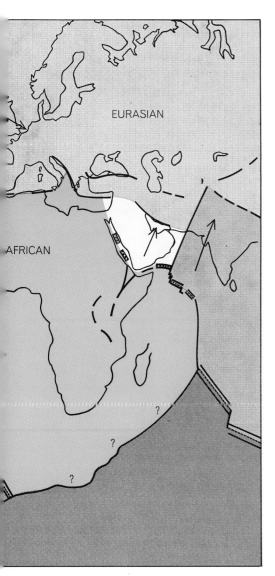

the American and Eurasian plates and in the region south of Africa, it is hard to say just where the boundaries of the plates lie.

4,000 million years and then broke apart and started their wanderings during the past 100 million years. It is more likely that the processes we see today have always been in action and that all through geologic time there have been moving plates carrying continents. We must expect continents to have split many times and formed new oceans and sometimes to have collided and been welded together. We are only at the beginning of the study of pre-Tertiary events; anything that can be said is speculation and is to be taken only as an indication of where to look.

It is virtually certain that the Atlantic did not exist 150 million years ago. Long before that, in the Lower Paleozoic, 650 to 400 million years ago, there was an older ocean in which the sediments now in the Caledonian-Hercynian-Appalachian mountains of Europe and North America were laid down. Perhaps this ocean was closed long before the present Atlantic opened and separated the Appalachian Mountains of eastern North America from their continuation in northwestern Europe.

The Urals, if they are not unique among mountain ranges, are at least exceptional in being situated in the middle of a continent. There is some paleomagnetic evidence that Siberia is a mosaic of fragments that were not originally contiguous; perhaps the Urals were once near the borders of an ocean that divided Siberia from western Russia. Similarly, it is desirable to ask where the ocean was when the Rockies were being formed. A large part of California is moving rapidly northward, and the entire continent has overrun an ocean ridge; clearly the early Tertiary geography must have been very different from that of the present. Such questions are for the future and require that the ideas of moving plates be applied by those with a detailed knowledge of the various areas.

A history of the oceans does not necessarily require an account of the mechanism behind the observed phenomena. Indeed, no very satisfactory account can be given. The traditional view, put forward by Arthur Holmes and Felix A. Vening-Meinesz, supposes that the upper mantle behaves as a liquid when it is subjected to small forces for long periods and that differences in temperature under oceans and continents are sufficient to produce convection cells in the mantle—with rising currents under the mid-ocean ridges and sinking ones under the continents. These hypothetical cells would carry the plates along as on

a conveyor belt and would provide the forces needed to produce the split along the ridge. This view may be correct; it has the advantage that the currents are driven by temperature differences that themselves depend on the position of the continents. Such a back-coupling can produce complicated and varying motions.

On the other hand, the theory is implausible in that convection does not normally happen along lines. It certainly does not happen along lines broken by frequent offsets, as the ridge is. Also it is difficult to see how the theory applies to the plate between the Mid-Atlantic Ridge and the ridge in the Indian Ocean. This plate is growing on both sides, and since there is no intermediate trench the two ridges must be moving apart. It would be odd if the rising convection currents kept exact pace with them. An alternative theory is that the sinking part of the plate, which is denser than the hotter surrounding mantle, pulls the rest of the plate after it. Again it is difficult to see how this applies to the ridge in the South Atlantic, where neither the African nor the American plate has a sinking part.

Another possibility is that the sinking plate cools the neighboring mantle and produces convection currents that move the plates. This last theory is attractive because it gives some hope of explaining the almost enclosed seas, such as the Sea of Japan. These seas have a typical oceanic floor except that the floor is overlain by several kilometers of sediment. Their floors have probably been sinking for long periods. It seems possible that a sinking current of cooled mantle material on the upper side of the plate might be the cause of such deep basins. The enclosed seas are an important feature of the earth's surface and urgently require explanation; in addition to the seas that are developing at present behind island arcs there are a number of older ones of possibly similar origin, such as the Gulf of Mexico, the Black Sea and perhaps the North Sea.

The ideas set out in this attempt at a history of the ocean have developed in the past 10 years. What we have is a sketch of the outlines of a history; a mass of detail needs to be filled in and many major features are quite uncertain. Nonetheless, there is a stage in the development of a theory when it is most attractive to study and easiest to explain, that is while it is still simple and successful and before too many details and difficulties have been uncovered. This is the interesting stage at which plate theory now stands.

III

The Atmosphere and the Ocean

The Atmosphere and the Ocean

R. W. STEWART

The two are inextricably linked. The ocean's circulation is driven by wind and by density differences that largely depend on the air. The atmospheric heat engine, in turn, is largely driven by the sea

The atmosphere drives the great ocean circulations and strongly affects the properties of seawater; to a large extent the atmosphere in turn owes its nature to and derives its energy from the ocean. Indeed, there are few phenomena of physical oceanography that are not somehow dominated by the atmosphere, and there are few atmospheric phenomena for which the ocean is unimportant. It is therefore hard to know where to start a discussion of the interactions of the atmosphere and the ocean, since in a way everything depends on everything else. One must break into this circle somewhere, and arbitrarily I shall begin by considering some of the effects of wind on ocean water.

When wind blows over water, it exerts a force on the surface in the direction of the wind. The mechanism by which it does so is rather complex and is far from being completely understood, but that it does it is beyond dispute. The ocean's response to this force is immensely complicated by a number of factors. The fact that the earth is rotating is of overriding importance. The presence of continental barriers across the natural directions of flow of the ocean complicates matters further. Finally there is the fact that water is a fluid, not a solid.

To simplify the picture somewhat, let us start by looking at what would happen to a slab of material resting on the surface of the earth. Let us further assume that the slab can move without friction. Consider the result of a sharp, brief impulse that sets the slab moving, say, due north [*see top illustration on page 32*]. Looked at by an observer on a rotating earth, any moving object is subject to a "Coriolis acceleration" directed exactly at a right angle to its motion. The magnitude of the acceleration increases with both the speed of the object's mo-

tion and the vertical component of the earth's rotation, and in the Northern Hemisphere it is directed to the right of the motion. An acceleration at right angles to the velocity is just what is required to cause motion in a circle, and in the illustration the center of the circle is due east of the original position of the slab. A circular motion of this kind is called an inertial oscillation, and something of this nature may sometimes happen in the ocean, since inertial oscillations are frequently found when careful observations are made with current meters.

An inertial oscillation requires exactly half a pendulum day for a full circle. (A pendulum day is the time required for a complete revolution of a Foucault pendulum. Like the Coriolis effect, it depends on the vertical component of the earth's rotation and therefore varies with latitude, being just under 24 hours at the poles and increasing to several days close to the Equator. To be precise, it is one sidereal—or star time—day divided by the sine of the latitude.) If there were a small amount of friction, the slab would gradually spiral to the center of the circle. Pushing it toward the north thus causes it to end up displaced to the east [*see bottom illustration on page 32*]. More generally, in the Northern Hemisphere a particle is moved to the right of the direction in which it is impelled, and in the Southern Hemisphere it is moved to the left.

Let us turn to what happens to our frictionless slab if, instead of giving it a short impulse, we give it a steady thrust. Again assume that the force is toward the north [*see upper illustration on page 33*]. Under the influence of this force the slab accelerates toward the north, but as soon as it starts to move it comes under the influence of the Coriolis effect

and its motion is deflected (in the Northern Hemisphere) to the right—to the east. As long as the slab has at least some component of velocity toward the north the force will continue to add energy to it and its speed will continue to increase. After a quarter of a pendulum day, however, it will be moving due east. In this position the applied force (which is to the north) is pushing at a right angle to the velocity (east), opposing the influence of the Coriolis effect, which is now trying to turn the slab toward the south.

If there has been no loss of energy because of friction, the slab is moving fast enough so that the Coriolis effect dominates, and it turns toward the south. Now there is a component of velocity opposing the applied force, which acts as a brake and takes energy from the motion. At the end of half a pendulum day the process has gone far enough to bring the slab to a full stop, at which point it is directly east of its starting point. If the force continues, it will again accelerate toward the north and the entire process is repeated, so that the slab performs a series of these looping (cycloidal) motions, each loop taking half a pendulum day to execute. Overall, then, a steady force on a frictionless body resting on a rotating earth causes it to move at right angles to the direction of the force. What is happening is that the force is balanced—on the average—by the Coriolis effect.

Now let us look at the situation when there is a certain amount of friction between the slab and the underlying surface [*see lower illustration on page 33*]. Any frictional drag reduces the speed attained by the slab, reducing the Coriolis effect until it is no longer entirely able to overcome the driving force. As a result if the force is toward the north, the slab will move in a more or less north-

OCEAN AND ATMOSPHERE, the two thin fluid films in which life is sustained and whose nature and motion determine the environment, dominate this color photograph of the watery hemisphere of the earth. The picture was made on January 21, 1968, by a spin-scan camera on NASA's Applications Technology Satellite 3, in synchronous orbit 22,300 miles above the Pacific Ocean. The camera experiment was proposed and developed by Verner E. Suomi and Robert J. Parent of the University of Wisconsin's Space Science and Engineering Center. As the camera spins it scans a 2.2-mile-wide strip across the earth, then steps down in latitude and scans another strip; in about 25 minutes a 2,400-strip picture is completed. What the camera transmits to the earth is an electrical signal representing the amount of green, red and blue light in each successive picture element, and from these signals a color negative is built up at the receiving station. Such photographs yield information on the interrelation of atmospheric and oceanic phenomena. In this picture, for example, the convective pattern over the southeastern Pacific indicates that air heated by the sea is rising.

Wind force: 4   Wind speed: 5½   Wave period: 5   Wave height: 1

Wind force: 5   Wind speed: 11½   Wave period: 6   Wave height: 2

Wind force: 6   Wind speed: 13   Wave period: 7   Wave height: 3

Wind force: 8   Wind speed: 18   Wave period: 6   Wave height: 5

Wind force: 9   Wind speed: 21   Wave period: 9   Wave height: 8

Wind force: 10   Wind speed: 27   Wave period: 9   Wave height: 7

easterly direction—more northerly if the friction is large, more easterly if it is small.

A body of water acts much like a set of such slabs, one on top of the other [*see illustration on page 34*]. Each slab is able to move largely independently of the others except for the frictional forces among them. If the top slab is pushed by the wind, it will, in the Northern Hemisphere, move in a direction somewhat to the right of the wind. It will exert a frictional force on the second slab down, which will then be set in motion in a direction still farther to the right. At each successive stage the force is somewhat reduced, so that not only does the direction change but also the speed is a bit less. A succession of such effects produces velocities for which the direction spirals as the depth increases. It is known as the Ekman spiral, after the pioneering Swedish oceanographer V. Walfrid Ekman, who first discussed it soon after the beginning of the century. At a certain depth both the current and the frictional forces associated with it become negligibly small. The entire layer above that depth, in which friction is important, is termed the Ekman layer. Since there is negligible friction between the Ekman layer and the water lying under it, the Ekman layer as a whole behaves like the frictionless slab discussed above: its average velocity must be at a right angle to the wind.

The frictional mechanism, which involves turbulence, has proved to be extraordinarily difficult to study either theoretically or through observations, and surprisingly little is known about it. The surface flow does appear to be somewhat to the right of the wind. Primitive theoretical calculations predict that its direction should be 45 degrees from the

EFFECT OF WIND on the surface of the sea is shown in a series of photographs made by the Meteorological Service of Canada. Much of the wind's momentum goes into generating waves rather than directly into making currents. The change in the surface as the wind increases is primarily a change in scale, except for the effect of surface tension: the waves break up more, making more whitecaps. For each photograph the wind force is given according to the Beaufort scale; the wind speed is given in meters per second, the wave period in seconds and the wave height in meters. (In the final photograph the waves are only about half as large as they might become if the force-10 wind, which had blown for less than nine hours, were to continue to blow.)

wind, but this theory is certainly inapplicable in detail. More complicated theoretical models have been attempted, but since almost nothing is known of the nature of turbulence in the presence of a free surface these models rest on weak ground. An educated guess, supported by rather flimsy observational evidence, suggests that the angle is much smaller, perhaps nearer to 10 degrees. All that seems fairly certain is that the average flow in the Ekman layer must be at a right angle to the wind and that there must be some kind of spiral in the current directions. We also believe the bottom of the Ekman layer lies 100 meters or so deep, within a factor of two or three. Of the details of the spiral, and of the turbulent mechanisms that determine its nature, we know very little indeed.

This Ekman-layer flow has some important fairly direct effects in several parts of the world. For example, along the coasts of California and Peru the presence of coastal mountains tends to deflect the low-level winds so that they blow parallel to the coast. Typically, in each case, they blow toward the Equator, and so the average Ekman flow—to the right off California and to the left off Peru—is offshore. As the surface water is swept away deeper water wells up to replace it. The upwelling water is significantly colder than the sun-warmed surface waters, somewhat to the discomfort of swimmers (and, since it is also well fertilized compared with the surface water, to the advantage of fishermen and birds).

The total amount of flow in the directly driven Ekman layer rarely exceeds a couple of tons per second across each meter of surface. That represents a substantial flow of water, but it is much less than the flow in major ocean currents. These are driven in a different way—also by the wind, but indirectly. To see how this works let us take a look at the North Atlantic [*see bottom illustration on page 35*]. The winds over this ocean, although they vary a good deal from time to time, have a most persistent characteristic: near 45 degrees north latitude or thereabouts the westerlies blow strongly from west to east, and at about 15 degrees the northeast trades blow, with a marked east-to-west component. The induced Ekman flow is to the right in each case, so that in both cases the water is pushed toward the region known as the Sargasso Sea, with its center at 30 degrees north. This "gathering together of the waters" leads not so much to a piling up (the surface level is only about a meter higher at

the center than at the edges) as a pushing down.

(If it were not for the continental boundaries, the piling up would be much more important. Because water tends to seek a level, the piled-up water would push north above 30 degrees and south below; the pushing force, like any other force in the Northern Hemisphere, would cause a flow to its right, so that in the northern part of the ocean a strong eastward flow would develop and in the southern part a strong westward one. On the earth as it now exists, however, these east-west flows are blocked by the continents; only in the Southern Ocean, around the Antarctic Continent, is such a flow somewhat free. In the absence of the continents the oceans, like the atmosphere, would be dominated by east-west motion. As it is, only a residue of such motion is possible, and it is the pushing down rather than the piling up of water that is important.)

The downward thrust of the surface waters presses down on the layers of water underneath [*see illustration on page 36*]. For practical purposes water is incompressible, so that pushing it down from the top forces it out at the sides. It must be remembered that this body of underlying water is rotating with the earth. As it is squeezed out laterally its radius of gyration, and therefore its moment of inertia, increase, and so its rate of rotation must slow. If it slows, however, the rotation no longer "fits" the rotation of the underlying earth. There are two possible consequences: either the water can rotate with respect to the earth or it can move to a different latitude where its newly acquired rotation *will* fit. It usually does the latter. Hence a body of water whose rotation has been slowed by being squashed vertically will usually move toward the Equator, where the vertical component of the earth's rotation is smaller; on the other hand, a body whose rotation has been speeded by being bulged up to replace water that has been swept away from the surface will usually move toward the poles.

In the band of water a couple of thousand miles wide along latitude 30 degrees this indirectly wind-driven flow moves water toward the Equator. Of course the regions of the ocean closer to the poles do not become empty of water; somewhere there must be a return flow. The returning water must also attain a rotation that fits the rotation of the underlying earth. If it flows north, it must gain counterclockwise rotation (or lose clockwise rotation). It does this by running in a strong current on the westward side of the ocean, changing its rotation

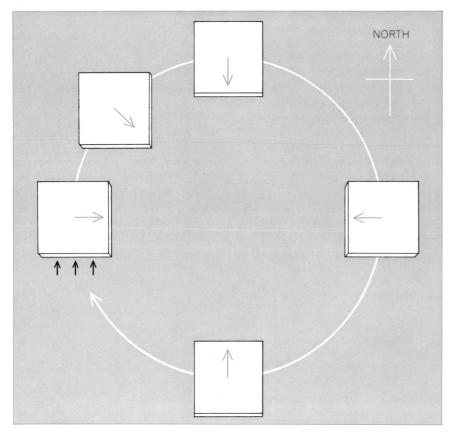

CORIOLIS ACCELERATION, caused by the earth's rotation, affects any object moving on the earth. It is directed at a right angle to the direction of motion (to the right in the Northern Hemisphere). If a frictionless slab is set in motion toward the north by a single impulse (*black arrows*), the Coriolis effect (*colored arrows*) moves the slab in a circle.

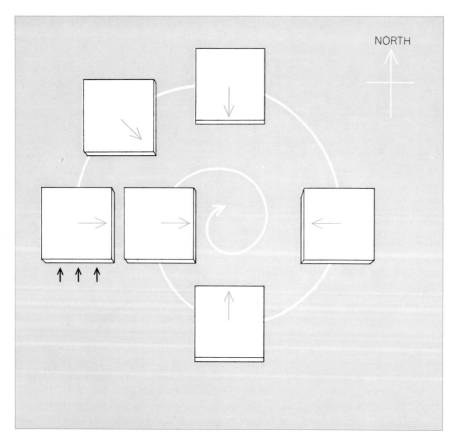

PRESENCE OF FRICTION causes the slab to slow down, spiraling in toward the center of the circle in the top illustration. A push to the north causes a spiral to the east.

by "rubbing its left shoulder" against the shore. The Gulf Stream is such a current; it is the return flow of water that was squeezed south by the wind-driven convergence of surface waters throughout the entire central North Atlantic. Most great ocean currents seem to be indirectly driven in this way.

It is worth noting that these return currents must be on the western side of the oceans (that is, off the eastern coasts of the land) in both hemispheres and regardless of whether the flow is northward or southward. The reason is that the earth's angular velocity of rotation is maximum counterclockwise to an observer looking down at the North Pole and maximum clockwise at the South Pole. Any south-flowing return current in either hemisphere must gain clockwise rotation (or lose counterclockwise rotation) if it is to fit when it arrives. It gains this rotation by friction on its right side, and so it must keep to the right—that is, to the west—of the ocean. On the other hand, a north-flowing return current must keep to the left—again the west!

This description of the general wind-driven circulation accords reasonably well with observations of the long-term characteristics of the ocean circulation. What happens on a shorter term, in response to changes of the atmospheric circulation and the wind-force pattern that results? The characteristic time constant of the Ekman layer is half a pendulum day, and there is every reason to believe this layer adjusts itself within a day or so to changes in the wind field. The indirectly driven flow is much harder to deal with. Its time constant is of the order of years, and we have no clear understanding of how it adjusts; the indirectly driven circulation may still be responding, in ways that are not clear, for years after an atmospheric change.

So far the discussion has been qualitative. To make it quantitative we need to know two things: the nature of the wind over the ocean at each time and place and the amount of force the wind exerts on the surface. Meteorologists are getting better at the first question, although there are some important gaps in our detailed information, notably in the Southern Ocean and in the South Pacific.

Investigation of the second problem, that of the quantitative relation between the wind flow and the force on the surface, is becoming a scientific discipline in its own right. Turbulent flow over a boundary is a complex phenomenon for which there is no really complete theory even in simple laboratory cases. Nevertheless, a great deal of experimental data has been collected on flows over solid surfaces, both in the laboratory and in nature, so that from an engineering point of view at least the situation is fairly well understood. The force exerted on a surface varies with the roughness of that surface and approximately with the square of the wind speed at some fixed height above it. A wind of 10 meters per second (about 20 knots, or 22 miles per hour) measured at a height of 10 meters will produce a force of some 30 tons per square kilometer on a field of mown grass or of about 70 tons per square kilometer on a ripe wheat field. On a really smooth surface such as glass the force is only about 10 tons per square kilometer.

When the wind blows over water, the whole thing is much more complicated. The roughness of the water is not a given characteristic of the surface but depends on the wind itself. Not only that, the elements that constitute the roughness—the waves—themselves move more or less in the direction of the wind. Recent evidence indicates that a large portion of the momentum transferred from the air into the water goes into waves rather than directly into making currents in the water; only as the waves break, or otherwise lose energy, does their momentum

become available to generate currents or produce Ekman layers. Waves carry a substantial amount of both energy and momentum (typically about as much as is carried by the wind in a layer about one wavelength thick), and so the wave-generation process is far from negligible. So far we have no theory that accounts in detail for what we observe.

A violently wavy surface belies its appearance by acting, as far as the wind is concerned, as though it were very smooth. At 10 meters per second, recent measurements seem to agree, the force on the surface is quite a lot less than the force over mown grass and scarcely more than it is over glass; some observations in light winds of two or three meters per second indicate that the force on the wavy surface is less than it is on a surface as smooth as glass. In some way the motion of the waves seems to modify the airflow so that air slips over the surface even more freely than it would without the waves. This seems not to be the case at higher wind speeds, above about five meters per second, but the force remains strikingly low compared with that over other natural surfaces.

One serious deficiency is the fact that there are no direct observations at all in those important cases in which the wind speed is greater than about 12 meters per second and has had time and

fetch (the distance over water) enough to raise substantial waves. (A wind of even 20 meters per second can raise waves eight or 10 meters high—as high as a three-story building. Making observations under such circumstances with the delicate instruments required is such a formidable task that it is little wonder none have been reported.) Some indirect studies have been made by measuring how water piles up against the shore when driven by the wind, but there are many difficulties and uncertainties in the interpretation of such measurements. Such as they are, they indicate that the apparent roughness of the surface increases somewhat under high-wind conditions, so that the force on the surface increases rather more rapidly than as the square of the wind speed.

Assuming that the force increases at least as the square of the wind speed, it is evident that high-wind conditions produce effects far more important than their frequency of occurrence would suggest. Five hours of 60-knot storm winds will put more momentum into the water than a week of 10-knot breezes. If it should be shown that for high winds the force on the surface increases appreciably more rapidly than as the square of the wind speed, then the transfer of momentum to the ocean will turn out to be dominated by what happens during

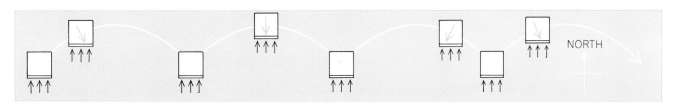

STEADY PUSH (*black arrows*), rather than a single impulse, is balanced, in the absence of friction, by the Coriolis effect (*colored arrows*), causing a series of loops. A steady force on a frictionless slab makes it move at a right angle to the direction of the force.

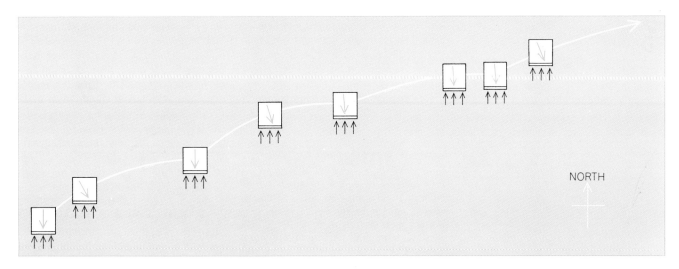

FRICTIONAL DRAG reduces the speed of the slab and thus of the Coriolis effect, which can no longer balance the driving force, and the amplitude of the loops is damped out gradually. A force toward the north therefore moves the slab toward the northeast.

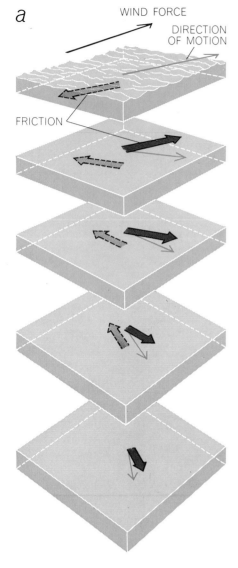

a

WIND FORCE

DIRECTION OF MOTION

FRICTION

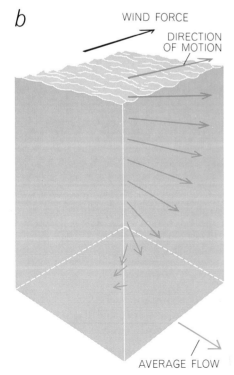

b

WIND FORCE

DIRECTION OF MOTION

AVERAGE FLOW

the occasional storm rather than by the long-term average winds.

It is tempting to try to infer high-wind behavior from what we know about lower wind speeds. Certainly the shapes of wavy surfaces appear nearly the same notwithstanding the size of the waves—as long as one disregards waves less than about five centimeters long, which are strongly affected by surface tension. Yet, curious as it may seem, the only thing that makes one wind-driven wave field different in any fundamental way from another is surface tension, even though it directly affects only these very short waves. Indeed, surface tension is the basis of the entire Beaufort wind scale, which depends on the number and nature of whitecaps; only the fact that the surface tension is better able to hold the surface together at low wind speeds than at high speeds enables us to see a qualitative difference in the nature of the sea surface at different wind speeds [*see illustration on page 30*]. Otherwise the waves would look just the same except for a difference in scale. If we were sure we could ignore surface-tension effects, then we could calculate the force the wind would exert at high wind speeds on the basis of data obtained at lower speeds, but one should be extremely cautious about such calculations, at least until some confirming measurements are available.

Whereas the ocean seems primarily to be driven by surface forces, the atmosphere is a heat engine that makes use of heat received from the sun to develop the mechanical energy of its motion. Any heat engine functions by accepting thermal energy at a comparatively high temperature, discharging some of this thermal energy at a lower temperature and transforming the rest into mechanical energy. The atmosphere does this by absorbing energy at or near its base and radiating it away from much cooler high levels. A substantial proportion of the required heating from below comes from the ocean.

This energy comes in two forms. If

BODY OF WATER can be thought of as a set of slabs (*a*), the top one driven by the wind and each driving the one below it by friction. At each stage the speed of flow is reduced and (in the Northern Hemisphere) directed more to the right. This "Ekman spiral" persists until friction becomes negligible. The "Ekman layer" in which this takes place (*b*) behaves like the frictionless slabs in the preceding illustrations. Its average flow is at right angle to wind driving it.

cooler air blows over warmer water, there is a direct heat flow into the air. What is usually more important, though, is the evaporation of water from the surface into the air. Evaporation causes cooling, that is, it removes heat, in this case from the surface of the water. When the moisture-laden air is carried to a high altitude, where expansion under reduced atmospheric pressure causes it to cool, the water vapor may recondense into water droplets and the heat that was given up by the surface of the water is transferred to the air. If the cloud that is formed evaporates again, as it sometimes does, the atmosphere gains no net thermal energy. If the water falls to the surface as rain or snow, however, then there has been a net gain and it is available to drive the atmosphere. Typically the heat gained by the atmosphere through this evaporation-condensation process is considerably more than the heat gained by direct thermal transfer through the surface.

Virtually everywhere on the surface of the ocean, averaged over a year, the ocean is a net source of heat to the atmosphere. In some areas the effect is much more marked than in others. For example, some of the most important return currents, such as the Gulf Stream in the western Atlantic and the Kuroshio Current in the western Pacific off Japan, contain very warm water and move so rapidly that the water has not cooled even when it arrives far north of the tropical and subtropical regions where it gained its high temperature. At these northern latitudes the characteristic wind direction is from the west, off the continent. In winter, when the continents are cold, air blowing from them onto this abnormally warm water receives great quantities of heat, both by direct thermal transfer and in the form of water vapor.

The transfer of heat and water vapor depends on a disequilibrium at the interface of the water and the air. Within a millimeter or so of the water the air temperature is not much different from that of the surface water, and the air is nearly saturated with water vapor. The small differences are nevertheless crucial, and the lack of equilibrium is maintained by the mixing of air near the surface with air at higher levels, which is typically appreciably cooler and lower in water-vapor content. The mixing mechanism is a turbulent one, the turbulence gaining its energy from the wind. The higher the wind speed is, the more vigorous the turbulence is and therefore the higher the rates of heat and moisture transfer are. These rates tend to increase linearly with the wind speed, but even less is known about the details of this phenomenon than about the wind force on water. One source of complication is the fact that, as I mentioned above, the wind-to-water transfer of momentum is effected partly by wave-generation mechanisms. When the wind makes waves, it must transfer not only momentum but also important amounts of energy—energy that is not available to provide the turbulence needed to produce the mixing that would effect the transfer of heat and water vapor.

At fairly high wind speeds another phenomenon arises that may be of considerable importance. I mentioned that when surface tension is no longer able to hold the water surface together at high wind speeds, spray droplets blow off the top of the waves. Some of these drops fall back to the surface, but others evaporate and in doing so supply water vapor to the air. They have another important role: The tiny residues of salt that are left over when the droplets of seawater evaporate are small enough and light enough to be carried upward by the turbulent air. They act as nuclei on which condensation may take place, and so they play a role in returning to the atmosphere the heat that is lost in the evaporation process.

The ocean's great effect on climate is illustrated by a comparison of the temperature ranges in three Canadian cities, all at about the same latitude but with very different climates [*see top illustration at right*]. Victoria is a port on the southern tip of Vancouver Island, on the eastern shore of the Pacific Ocean; Winnipeg is in the middle of the North American land mass; St. John's is on the island of Newfoundland, jutting into the western Atlantic. The most striking climatic difference among the three is the enormous temperature range at Winnipeg compared with the two coastal cities. The range at St. John's, although much less, is still greater than at Victoria, probably because at St. John's the air usually blows from the direction of the continent and the effect of the water is somewhat less dominant than at Victoria, which typically receives its air directly from the ocean. St. John's is colder than Victoria because it is surrounded by cold water of the Labrador Current.

The influence of the ocean is associated with its enormous thermal capacity. Every day, on the average, the earth absorbs from the sun and reradiates into space enough heat to raise the temperature of the entire atmosphere nearly two degrees Celsius (three degrees Fahrenheit). Yet the thermal ca-

	VICTORIA	WINNIPEG	ST. JOHN'S
MEAN JULY MAXIMUM	68	80.1	68.9
MEAN JANUARY MINIMUM	35.6	−8.1	18.5

MODERATING EFFECT of the ocean on climate is illustrated by a comparison of the temperature range (in degrees Fahrenheit) at three Canadian cities. The range between minimums and maximums is much greater at Winnipeg than at coastal Victoria or St. John's.

pacity of the atmosphere is equivalent to that of only the top three meters of the ocean, or only a few percent of the 100 meters or so of ocean water that is heated in summer and cooled in winter. (The great bulk of ocean water, more than 95 percent of it, is so deep that surface heating does not penetrate, and its temperature is independent of season.) If the ocean lost its entire heat supply for a day but continued to give up heat in a normal way, the temperature of the upper 100 meters would drop by only about a tenth of a degree.

Compared with the land, the ocean heats slowly in summer and cools slowly in winter, so that its temperature is much less variable. Moreover, because air has so much less thermal capacity, when it blows over water it tends to come to the water temperature rather than vice versa. For these reasons maritime climates are much more equable than continental ones.

Although the ocean affects the atmosphere's temperature more than the atmosphere affects the ocean's, the ocean is cooled when it gives up heat to the atmosphere. The density of ocean water is controlled by two factors, temperature and salinity, and evaporative cooling tends to make the water denser by affecting both factors: it lowers the temperature and, since evaporation removes water but comparatively little salt, it also increases the salinity. If surface water becomes denser than the water underlying it, vigorous vertical convective mixing sets in. In a few places in the ocean the cooling at the surface can be so intense that the water will sink and mix to great depths, sometimes right to the bottom. Such occurrences are rare both in space and in time, but once cold water has reached great depths it is heated from above very slowly, and so it tends to stay deep for a long time with little change in temperature; there is some evidence of water that has remained cold and deep in the ocean for more than

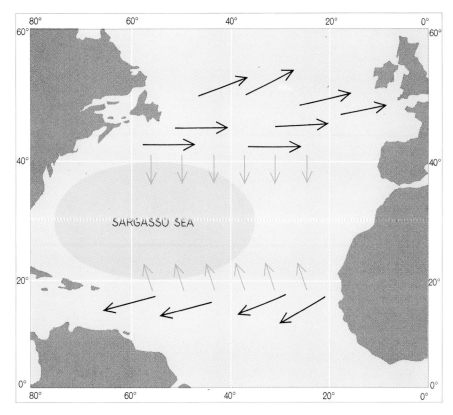

PREVAILING-WIND DIRECTIONS (*black arrows*) and the resulting Ekman-layer flows (*colored arrows*) in the North Atlantic drive water into the region of the Sargasso Sea.

1,000 years. With this length of residence not much of the heavy, cold water needs to be produced every year for it to constitute, as it does, the bulk of the ocean water.

The sinking of water cooled at the surface is one aspect of another important feature of the ocean: the flow induced by differences in density, which is to say the flow induced principally by temperature and salt content. This thermohaline circulation of the ocean is in addition to the wind-driven circulation discussed earlier.

In its thermohaline aspects the ocean itself acts as a heat engine, although it is far less efficient than the atmosphere. Roughly speaking, the ocean can be divided into two layers: a rather thin upper one whose density is comparatively low because it is warmed by the sun, and a thick lower one, a fraction of a percent denser and composed of water only a few degrees above the freezing point that has flowed in from those few areas where it is occasionally created. Somewhere—either distributed over the ocean or perhaps only locally near the shore and in other special places—there is mixing between these layers. The mixing is of such a nature that the cold deep water is mixed into the warm upper water rather than the other way around,

that is, the cold water is added to the warm from the bottom [see upper illustration on page 38]. Once the water is in the upper layer its motion is largely governed by the wind-driven circulation, although density differences still play a role. In one way or another some of this surface water arrives at a location and time at which it is cooled sufficiently to sink again and thus complete the circulation.

This picture can be rounded out by consideration of the effects of the earth's rotation, which are in some ways quite surprising. The deep water that mixes into the upper layer must have a net upward motion. (The motion is far too

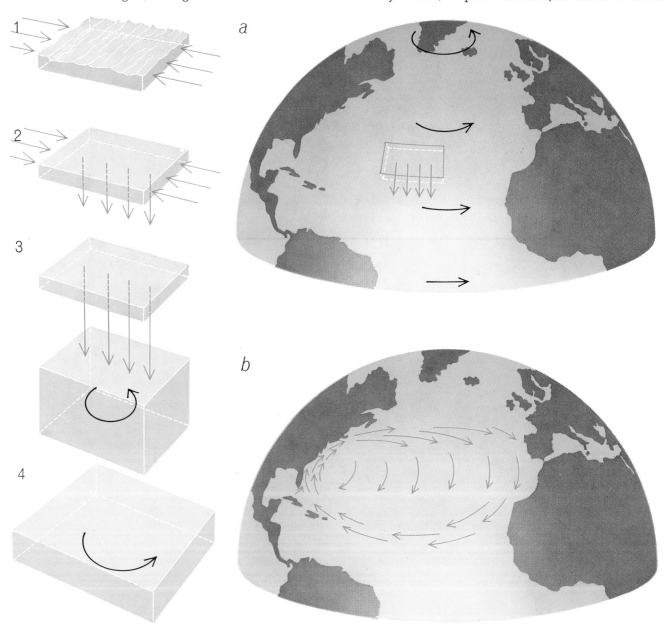

MAJOR CURRENTS are generated by a mechanism involving the Ekman-layer flow and the earth's rotation. The Ekman-layer inflow shown in the preceding illustration (1) produces a downflow (2) that presses on the underlying water (3), squeezing it outward (4) and thus reducing its rate of rotation (curved black arrow). There is a rate of rotation appropriate to each latitude, and when the rotation of a body of water is reduced, it must move (colored arrows) toward the Equator until its new rotation "fits" (a). For this reason there is a general movement of water from the mid-latitudes toward the Equator (b). That water must be replaced, and the water replacing it must have the proper rotation. This is accomplished by a return flow that runs along the western shore of the ocean, changing its rotation by "rubbing its shoulder" against the coast, as the Gulf Stream does in the Atlantic Ocean.

small to measure, only a few meters per year, but we infer its existence indirectly.) To make possible this upward flow there must be a compensating lateral inflow. Remember that on the rotating earth this lateral inflow results in an increase in speed of rotation, and so for it to continue to fit the rotation of the underlying earth the water must move toward the nearest pole; it must flow away from the equatorial regions. Yet the source of this cold deep water is at high latitudes! How does it get near the Equator to supply the demand?

The answer is similar to the one for the wind-driven circulation: The cold water must flow in a western boundary current, in order to gain the proper rotation as it moves [*see lower illustration on next page*]. There is some direct evidence of the inferred concentrated western boundary current in the North Atlantic, and there are hints of it in the South Pacific, but most of the rest is based on inference. There seems to be no source of cold deep water in the North Pacific, so that the deep water there must come from Antarctic regions.

We have seen that the atmosphere drives the ocean and that heat supplied from the ocean is largely instrumental in releasing energy for the atmosphere. There is a great deal of feedback between the two systems. The atmospheric patterns determine the oceanic flows, which in turn influence where—and how much—heat is released to the atmosphere. Further, the atmospheric flow systems determine how much cloud cover there will be over certain parts of the ocean and therefore how much—and where—the ocean will be heated. The system is not a particularly stable one. Every locality has its abnormally cold or mild winters and its abnormally wet or dry summers. The persistence of such anomalies over several months almost certainly involves the ocean, because the characteristic time constants of purely atmospheric phenomena are simply too short. Longer-term climatological variations such as the "little ice age" that lasted for about 40 years near the beginning of the 19th century are even more likely to have involved changes in the ocean's circulation. And then there are the more dramatic events of the great Pleistocene glaciations.

There are any number of theories for these events and, since experts disagree, it is incumbent on the rest of us to refrain from dogmatic statements. Nevertheless, it does not seem impossible that the ocean-atmosphere system has a number of more or less stable configurations.

INFRARED IMAGERY delineates the temperature structure of bodies of water and is used to study currents and wave patterns. This image of the shoulder of the Gulf Stream is from the Antisubmarine Warfare Environmental Prediction Services Project of the Naval Oceanographic Office. It was made by an airborne scanner at low altitude and shows several hundred yards of the boundary between the warm current and cooler water off Cape Hatteras. The range is from about 13 to 21 degrees Celsius, with the warm water darker.

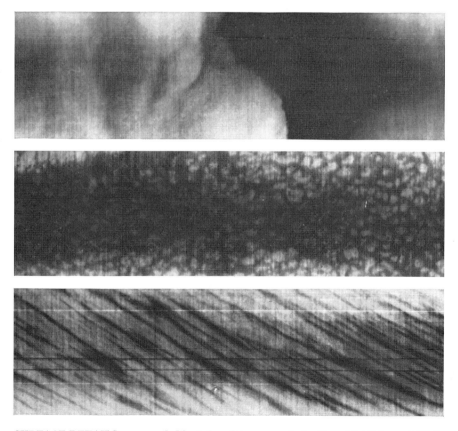

SURFACE DETAILS are revealed by infrared images made by E. D. McAlister and W. L. McLeish of the Scripps Institution of Oceanography. In these prints warm water is lighter in tone and cold water darker; the general lightening that is noticeable at the top and bottom of each strip is the result of increased sky reflectivity at large angles from the vertical. The top print shows an ocean "front," a temperature discontinuity between warm water (*left*) and colder water (*right*). The middle print shows a convective pattern. The bottom print shows streaks of cooler water that have become lined up in the direction of the wind.

That is, there may be a number of different patterns in which the atmosphere can drive the ocean in such a way that the ocean releases heat to the atmosphere in the right quantity and at the right places to allow the pattern to continue. Of course the atmosphere is extremely turbulent, so that its equilibrium is constantly being disturbed. If the system is stable, then forces must come into play that tend to restore conditions after each such disturbance. If there are a number of different stable patterns, however, it is possible that a particularly large disturbance might tip the system from one stable condition to another.

One can imagine a gambler's die lying on the floor of a truck running over a rough road; the die is stable on any of its six faces, so that in spite of bouncing and vibration the same face usually remains up—until a particularly big bump jars it so that it lands with a different face up, whereupon it is stable in its new position. It seems not at all impossible that the ocean-atmosphere system behaves something like this. Perhaps in recent years we have been bouncing along with, say, a four showing. Perhaps 200 years ago the die flipped over to three for a moment, then flipped back to four. It could one day jounce over to a snake eye and bring a new ice age!

POLE ⟵   EQUATOR ⟶

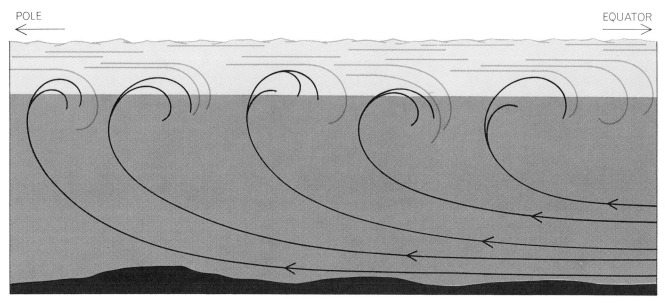

THERMOHALINE CIRCULATION, the flow induced by density rather than wind action, begins with the creation of dense, cold water that sinks to great depths. Under certain conditions this deep water mixes upward into the warm surface layer (*color*) as shown here. As it moves up, this water increases its rotation and so it must move generally from the Equator toward the two poles.

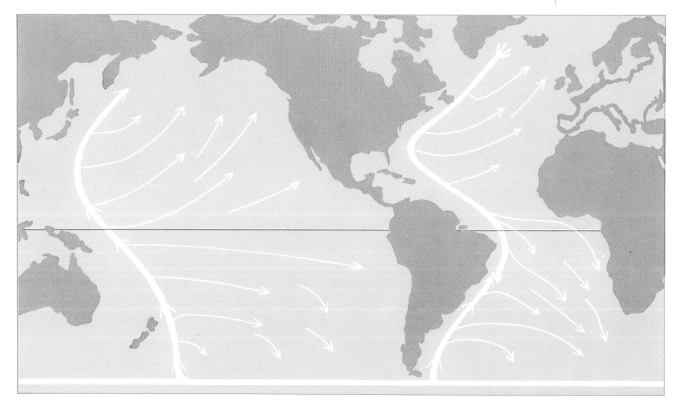

COLD DEEP WATER must flow in western boundary currents in order to arrive at the Equator and thus be able to move poleward as it mixes upward. Details of deep circulation are still almost unknown and the chart is intended only to suggest its approximate directions. There is some evidence of such boundary currents in the North Atlantic and there are some hints in the South Pacific.

IV

The Continental Shelves

The Continental Shelves

K. O. EMERY

The shallow regions adjacent to the continents are equal in extent to 18 percent of the earth's total land area. They are alternately exposed and drowned as the continental glaciers advance and retreat

The continental shelves were the first part of the sea floor that was studied by man, chiefly as an aid to navigation and fishing. Perhaps the earliest recorded observation was one made by Herodotus about 450 B.C. "The nature of the land of Egypt is such," he wrote, "that when a ship is approaching it and is yet one day's sail from the shore, if a man try the sounding, he will bring up mud even at a depth of 11 fathoms." A more recent example is found in the diary of a 19th-century seaman: "An old captain once told me to take a cast of the lead at 4 a.m. We were bound to Hull from the Baltic. He came on deck before breakfast and on showing him the arming of the lead, which consisted of sand and small pebbles, I was surprised to see him take a small pebble and put it in his mouth. He tried to break it with his teeth. I was very curious and asked him why he did so. He told me that the small pebbles were called Yorkshire beans, and if you could break them you were toward the westward of the Dogger Bank; if you could not, you were toward the eastward."

Fishing success often depends on knowledge of the kind of bottom frequented by particular fish and on the avoidance of rocky areas that can catch and tear nets. As a result governmental agencies routinely chart bottom topography and materials to aid the fishing industry, but the successful fisherman generally keeps much additional information to himself. Similarly, the production of oil and gas from the continental shelves during the past two decades has led governmental and international agencies to make broad geological surveys, which help to guide the oil industry to the areas of greatest economic promise. The oil companies make studies that are much more detailed and so expensive that the results are considered proprietary, at least until after exploitation rights are secured.

During World War II submarines took a large toll of the ships that crossed the continental shelves, mainly at the approaches of ports. The effectiveness of acoustical detection equipment on submarine hunting ships was much increased by a knowledge of bottom materials and their effects: long ranges over sand, short ones over mud, confusing echoes over rock or coral. Accordingly charts of bottom sediments were compiled by the American and German navies for many areas of the world. This problem had not arisen earlier because both submarines and the search gear of surface ships were too primitive during World War I, and it may not be important in the future owing to the greatly increased sophistication of submarines and to the different role they may play in any future war.

The conflict between disseminating information and keeping it secret is about what one would expect in an environment that is both economically and militarily important. The recent political interest in the sovereignty of the ocean is also to be expected, considering the way the economic potential of the shelves has often been exaggerated in recent years. Thus it is not surprising that there have been a number of proposals to redefine the continental shelf so as to extend it seaward to whatever distance and to whatever depth are necessary to give a nation access to the resources presumably lying or hidden there. In 1953, before the world developed its present large appetite for seafood and minerals, an international commission defined the continental shelf, shelf edge and continental borderland as: "The zone around the continent extending from the low-water line to the depth at which there is a marked increase of slope to greater depth. Where this increase occurs the term shelf edge is appropriate. Conventionally the edge is taken at 100 fathoms (or 200 meters), but instances are known where the increase of slope occurs at more than 200 or less than 65 fathoms. When the zone below the low-water line is highly irregular and includes depths well in excess of those typical of continental shelves, the term continental borderland is appropriate."

Somewhat similar, but shorter, definitions are presented by most textbooks of geology. Where a depth limit is given it is 100 fathoms, an inheritance from the time when navigational charts had only three depth contours: 10, 100 and 1,000 fathoms. On a global basis the edge of the continental shelf ranges in depth from 20 to 550 meters, with an average of 133 meters; the shelf ranges in width from zero to 1,500 kilometers, with an average of 78 kilometers [*see illustration on next two pages*].

CONTINENTAL SHELF in the Atlantic Ocean off Cape Hatteras is delineated by puffy clouds that show where cold surface water on the eastern edge of the shelf meets warmer surface water. The boundary is near the edge of the shelf, which at this point averages about 120 meters in depth. The picture also shows turbid water moving from Pamlico Sound into the ocean, where it is carried northward by a fringe of the Gulf Stream that lies atop the shelf. The photograph was taken from *Apollo 9* on March 12 of this year, at an altitude of 134 statute miles; the view extends 175 miles in the north-south direction. The astronauts on this mission were James A. McDivitt, David R. Scott and Russell L. Schweikart.

The continental shelves underlie only 7.5 percent of the total area of the oceans, but they are equal to 18 percent of the earth's total land area. A geological understanding of this huge region requires a knowledge of its topography, sediments, rocks and geologic structure. For nearly all shelves there is some information about topography; for perhaps a fourth of them something can be said about the surface sediments, but the rocks and geologic structure are known for less than 10 percent. Detailed knowledge is far less available. The best-known large areas are the ones off the U.S., eastern Canada, western Europe and Japan—in short, the shelves next to countries where scientific knowledge is well developed and freely disseminated. Smaller areas of knowledge are found where oil companies have worked (such as parts of northern South America, parts of Australia and the Persian Gulf) and where oceanographic institutions have conducted repeated operations (northwestern Alaska, the Gulf of California, northwestern Africa, the shelf off Argentina, the Red Sea and the Yellow Sea). Recently some developing countries have effectively closed their shelves to foreign scientific studies; these areas are fated to remain unknown and unexploited for the foreseeable future.

The information that is most costly and most difficult to obtain concerns the underlying rocks and the structural geology of the continental shelves. This information is essential for understanding the origin and most of the history of the shelves. Data about the surface topography and sediments, which are readily accessible, tell only the late history.

Samples of bedrock have been dredged from the surface of many shelves, mainly from the top of small projecting hills and the sides and heads of submarine canyons that incise the shelves. Additional rock samples have come from the top of the adjacent continental slopes. Care must be taken in deciding whether the rock samples are from outcrops, whether they are loose pieces that were deposited by ancient streams or glaciers, or whether they were rafted to their present location by ice, kelp, marine animals or man. The decision is usually based on the size of the piece, on the presence or absence of fresh fractures, on the similarity of lithologic types within a given dredging area or between adjacent dredging areas, and on the amount of tension of the dredge cable. It is helpful to have submarine

photographs, which may reveal rock outcrops in the dredging area. Rock also can be sampled by coring: by dropping or forcing a heavily weighted pipe into the bottom. This method can show the dip of the strata, and it can sample rock that is covered by sediments if the sediment is thin or if it is first removed by hydraulic jetting. A better but more expensive method of rock sampling is provided by well-drilling methods. Many holes have been drilled for geological information in shelf areas of structural interest; they provide good information on the sequence and depth of strata, the date of original deposition and geologic structure. In addition several thousand oil wells have been sunk into shelves,

but most have been drilled in abnormal geologic structures such as salt domes and folds.

Geophysical methods provide excellent, although indirect, data from which geological cross sections can be constructed. These methods include seismic reflection and refraction, as well as measurements of geomagnetism and gravity. Each method has its advantages, but the most generally successful one is seismic reflection. In practice a ship traverses the shelf and produces a loud acoustical signal in the water at intervals of a few seconds. The chief source of sound energy a few years ago was a chemical explosive, usually dynamite; other sources are now preferred because they are

CONTINENTAL SHELVES underlie about 7.5 percent of the total ocean; all together they occupy an area roughly equal to that of Europe and South America combined, or some 10 million square miles. The shelf is defined as the zone around a continent extending from

cheaper, easier to trigger accurately and greatly reduce the danger both to the operators on the ship and to the fish in the sea. These newer energy sources include electric spark, compressed air and propane gas. Although part of the sound energy is reflected from the sea floor, much of it enters the bottom to be reflected upward from various layers of rock under the bottom. The reflected energy is received by hydrophones trailed behind the ship; the signal is amplified, filtered and recorded on continuously moving paper tapes. This method, termed continuous seismic-reflection profiling, is rapid and can yield information from depths of several kilometers under the sea floor, making it possible to construct geological cross sections. When the interpretations are supplemented by dredging or drilling, they provide the best information now available about the structure of continental shelves.

When existing geological and geophysical information is assembled on a worldwide basis, it shows that continental shelves can be classified into two main types by composition: those that are underlain by sedimentary strata and those underlain by igneous and metamorphic rocks. A large majority of the world's continental shelves mark the top surface of long, thick prisms of sedimentary strata [see illustration on next two pages]. Many of the prisms are held in position against the continents by long, narrow fault blocks. Such is true of almost the entire perimeter of the Pacific Ocean, where tectonic activity has also produced deep trenches that are parallel to the base of the continental slope. In some areas, such as the West Coast of the U.S., a single geologic dam is known to have extended for thousands of kilometers along the coast. Locally part of the dam rises above sea level to form the granitic Farallon Islands that lie immediately off San Francisco. These rocks are some 100 million years old, but they were thrust up to form the dam only about 25 million years ago. Elsewhere, as in the Yellow Sea of Asia, half a dozen such fault dams or fold dams

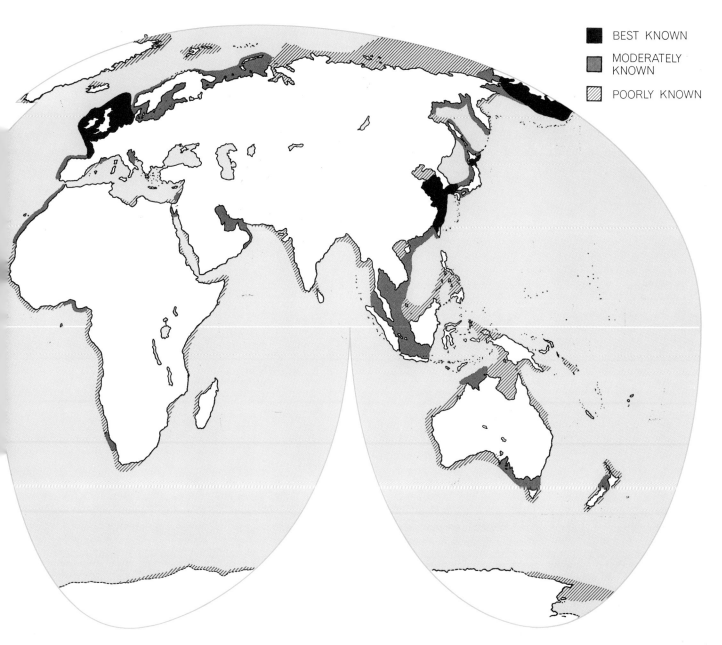

BEST KNOWN

MODERATELY KNOWN

POORLY KNOWN

the low-water line to the depth at which the ocean bottom slopes markedly downward. Conventionally the edge of the shelf is taken to lie at 100 fathoms, or 200 meters, but a more accurate average value for all continents is about 130 meters. Worldwide the shelf has an average width of 78 kilometers. The illustration indicates the present state of knowledge of the continental shelves of the world.

have risen in the last 500 million years or so, each dam in turn causing the ponding of sediments from the land. There was a similar dam off the entire length of the East Coast of the U.S. between 270 and 60 million years ago; in time the trench on its landward side was filled with sediments that subsequently spilled over the former dam to build a continental slope that is held in place only by the angle of rest of the sediments. That this angle is unstable is shown by numerous landslides and erosion features recorded in seismic profiles across the continental slope and rise.

The continental shelf off the western part of the Gulf Coast of the U.S. is held in place by a diapir dam: a dam formed by the upward movement of salt from a bed that is buried several kilometers deep and is about 150 million years old. Seismic profiles and dredgings show the presence of still another kind of dam in

the eastern Gulf of Mexico and off the southeastern coast of the U.S. This is an algal reef that dates from 130 million years ago and was succeeded by a coral reef off Florida at some time before 25 million years ago; even today the Florida keys are bordered by a living coral reef. Similar tectonic and biogenic dams elsewhere in the world have trapped huge quantities of sediments in the geological past.

Shelf areas underlain by igneous and metamorphic rocks are found on top of the tectonic dams. Off Maine, however, glacial erosion has removed the sedimentary rocks that once covered such a dam [*see illustration on pages 46 and 47*]. Other shelves underlain by igneous and metamorphic rocks are known, but most of them appear to be at high latitudes where glacial erosion has been effective. Nevertheless, even at high altitudes probably most of the shelves are

underlain by sedimentary rock. In a sense we can consider the shelves whose shape is chiefly due to glacial or wave erosion as youthful ones (or rejuvenated ones); the shelves that are mainly depositional, with a thick prism of sediments on top of igneous and metamorphic rocks, can be regarded as mature ones. The sediments have built the shelves upward during the concurrent sinking of the edges of the continents. Perhaps more important from the viewpoint of real estate, these sediments have increased the size of the continents, widening them as much as 800 kilometers in areas where rivers have brought much sediment from the land and where tectonic or other dams effectively prevent the escape of the sediment to the ocean basins. This dammed sediment, as well as the sediment held only by its angle of rest, has an estimated average thickness of about two kilometers, yielding a total

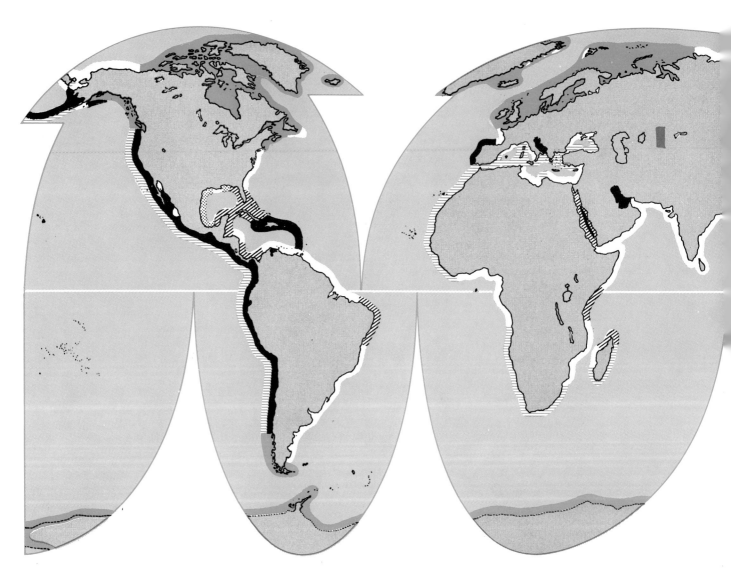

CHARACTER OF CONTINENTAL SHELF depends largely on how the shelf was formed. Six types of shelf, classified by origin, are indicated in this worldwide map. Many shelves are deposited behind three kinds of dams: tectonic dams, formed by geological uplift or upwelling of lava; reef dams, created by marine organisms, and diapir dams, which are pushed upward by salt domes.

volume of sedimentary strata under continental shelves of about 50 million cubic kilometers.

Perhaps the most dramatic period in the history of the continental shelves was the million-year passage of the Pleistocene epoch when the sea level changed in response to the waxing and waning of the continental glaciers. At their maximum the glaciers appear to have been so extensive as to have stored in the form of ice enough water to lower the surface of the ocean nearly 150 meters below the present level. Four major lowerings of the sea level were produced by the four main glaciations, with minor lowerings caused by secondary fluctuations of climate and ice volume. Limited investigations with special seismic equipment off the East Coast of the U.S. show four or five somewhat irregular acoustical reflecting surfaces near the top

of the shelf sediments. These reflecting surfaces probably can be explained by erosion and sand deposition at stages of low sea level. Cores from these beds probably would provide much interesting information about Pleistocene climates and Pleistocene chronology. For the present, however, our data for glacial effects on the continental shelf are restricted largely to surface sediments and topography.

About 50 years ago most textbooks of geology led the reader to believe that sediments became progressively finer in texture with distance from shore: gravel and sand at the shore, coarse sand grading to fine sand across the shelf, and finally silt and clay (the "mud line") at the shelf edge. Bottom-sediment charts compiled during World War II, however, showed that this simple pattern is very rare, and that the size of sediment grains is unrelated to the distance from

shore. The examination of actual samples showed that most of the shelves are floored with coarse sands that commonly are stained by iron and contain the empty shells of mollusks that live only close to shore in shallow depths. Broken shells or shell sand are particularly abundant at the outer edge of the shelf and on small submerged hills that are relatively inaccessible to detrital sediments. Some of these same areas contain glauconite and phosphorite, minerals that are precipitated from seawater, but so slowly that they are obscured or diluted beyond recognition where detrital minerals are present. The only areas that exhibit a consistent seaward decrease of grain size are those between the shore and depths of 10 or 20 meters—in short, whatever areas are shallow enough to be ruled by the waves. At greater depths the sediments are too deep to be reached by new supplies of sand. These sections

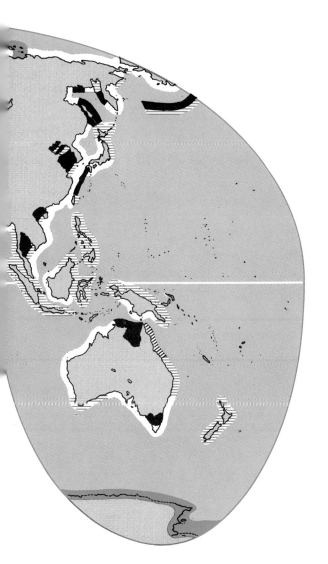

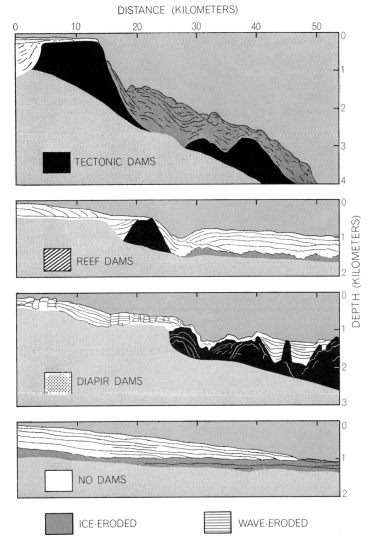

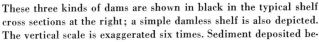

These three kinds of dams are shown in black in the typical shelf cross sections at the right; a simple damless shelf is also depicted. The vertical scale is exaggerated six times. Sediment deposited before formation of the dam is shaded gray; sediment deposited subsequently is unshaded. All four kinds of shelf structure may be eroded by waves (*hatched color on map*) or by ice (*solid color*).

of the shelves are also bypassed by contemporary silts and clays that remain in suspension en route to deeper or quieter waters.

The sediments on about 70 percent of the world's continental-shelf area have been laid down in the past 15,000 years, since the last glacial lowering of the sea level. The rest of the shelf is floored by silts at the mouths of large rivers, in quiet waters behind barriers and in shelf basins, by recent shell debris and by chemically deposited minerals. This means that when the sea level was low, the entire shelf was exposed and the rivers deposited sands on the then broader coastal plain and transported their silts and clays to the ocean. At that time ocean waves, with no shelf to reduce their height, were probably higher at the shore than they are today, with the result that shore sediments were probably coarser. The broad expanse of lowland favored the development of ponds and marshes, which were partly filled with debris from the forests and meadows that extended unbroken from the inland areas across what is now the sea floor. Freshwater peat now submerged in the ocean has been sampled at 10 sites off the eastern U.S. and at many other sites on the shore; similar peats have been found off Europe, Japan and elsewhere.

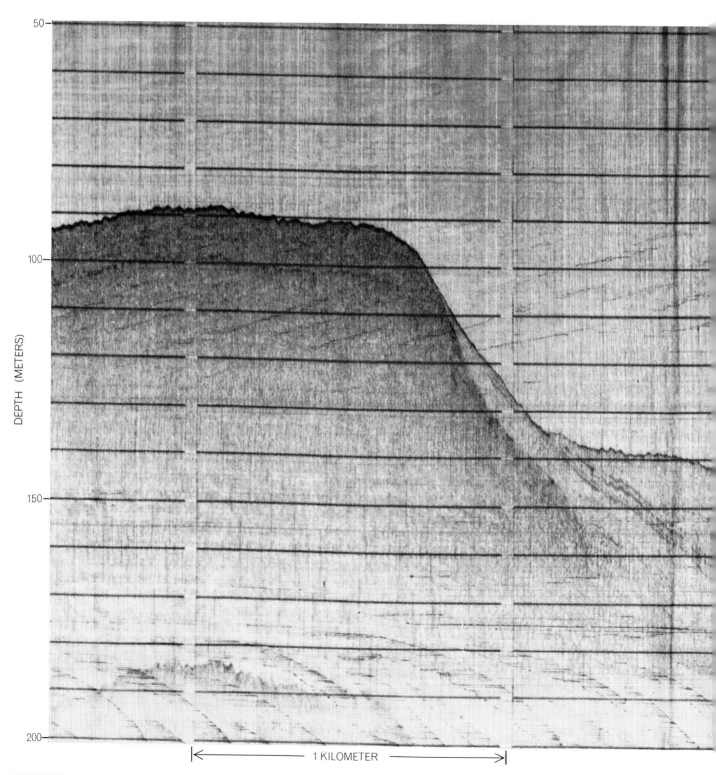

ICE-ERODED SHELF about 100 kilometers off the coast of Maine, landward of Georges Bank, is shown in this seismic-reflection record. The deep trough was gouged out of the basement rock by ice some 15,000 years ago during the last glaciation. Subsequently the trough

Pollen analysis shows a succession from tundra to boreal spruce and pine some 12,000 years ago, followed by oak and other Temperate Zone deciduous trees about 8,500 years ago; the deciduous trees flourished until the site was submerged. Birds once flew among the trees in many areas where fish now swim.

The vegetation attracted many animals, but only their heavier bones are preserved or are readily detected by dredging. Nearly 50 teeth of mammoths and mastodons have been collected off the East Coast of the U.S., along with the bones of the musk ox, giant moose, horse, tapir and giant ground sloth. Similar finds have been reported off Europe and Japan.

Carbon-14 dates have been obtained for more than 50 samples of shallow-water material from the shelf off the East Coast of the U.S. The materials include salt-marsh peat, oölites (concentrically banded calcium carbonate pellets that typically form only in warm, shallow, agitated seawater) and the shells of oysters and other mollusks (which live in only a few meters of water but whose empty shells are found as deep as 130 meters). The dates and depths make it possible to draw a curve showing the changes of sea level in an-

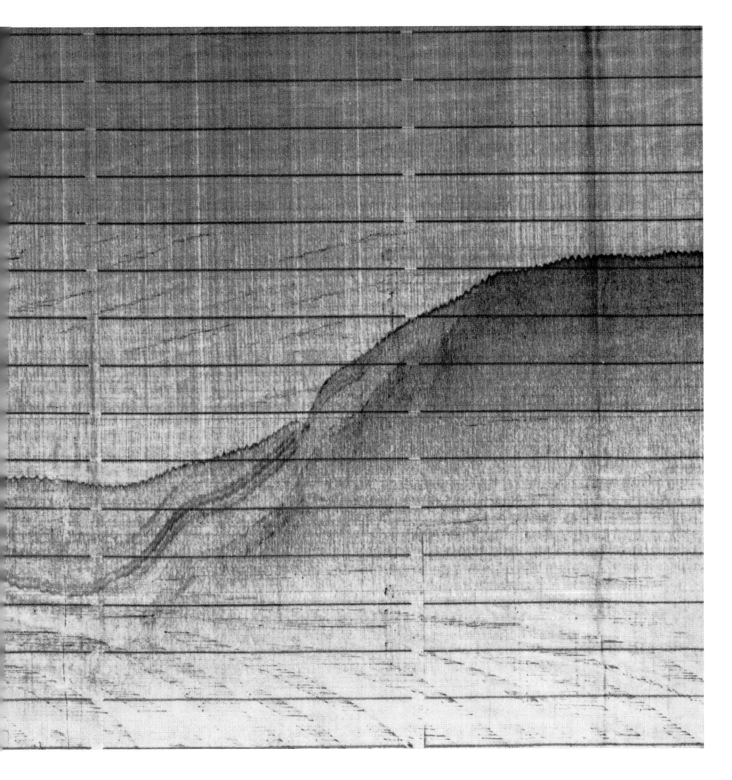

became filled with sediments about 30 meters thick. The recording was made this past July with high-frequency seismic equipment aboard the *Dolphin*, a vessel operated by the U.S. Geological Survey in cooperation with the Woods Hole Oceanographic Institution.

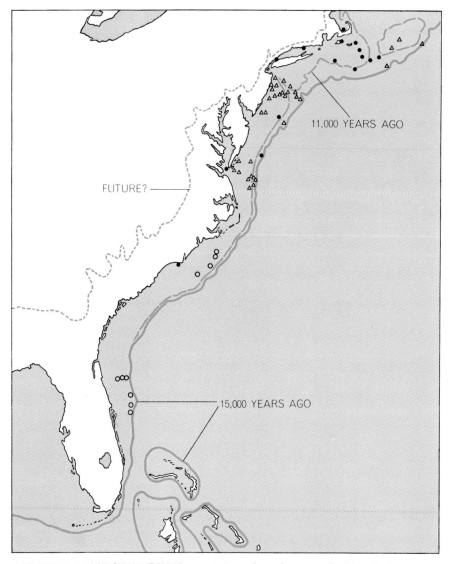

ATLANTIC COAST SHORELINE has varied greatly in the past and will undoubtedly continue to in the future. This illustration compares the shoreline of 15,000 and 11,000 years ago with the probable shoreline if all the ice at the poles were to melt. Confirmation that the continental shelf was once laid bare is found in discoveries of elephant teeth (*triangles*), freshwater peat (*dots*) and the shallow-water formations called oölites (*circles*).

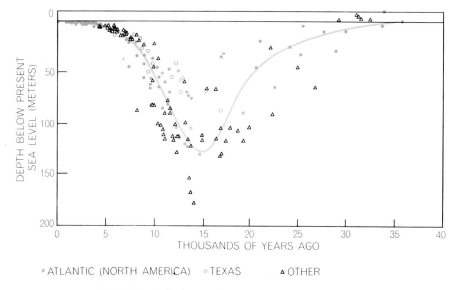

WORLDWIDE CHANGES IN SEA LEVEL can be inferred from the radiocarbon ages of shallow-water marine organisms and the depth at which they were recovered. Samples are from the Atlantic shelf of North America, the Texas shelf and other parts of the world. The depth inconsistency of the Texas samples implies that the shelf there has been uplifted.

cient times [*see bottom illustration at left*].

Apparently the sea was near its present level about 35,000 years ago and began to recede about 30,000 years ago. The level dropped by 130 meters or more 15,000 years ago; then it rose rather rapidly to within about five meters of the present level 5,000 years ago. The slow rise during the past 5,000 years has been documented by perhaps 100 carbon-14 dates for peat under existing salt marshes. Less complete sequences of dates for similar samples from elsewhere in the world show a sea-level curve resembling the one for the East Coast. Only the samples from the shelf in the western Gulf of Mexico provide a different curve, which suggests that this part of the gulf shelf was uplifted about 40 meters during the past 10,000 years.

Early men of the Clovis culture (characterized by fluted stone projectile points) appeared in North America some 12,000 years ago, when the sea level was still very low. What is more reasonable than to suppose such men ranged over the forested lowland that is now continental shelf? Game, fish and oysters were abundant. How were they to know or care that in a few thousand years the area was to be drowned by the advancing sea, any more than New Yorkers know or care that when the remaining glaciers melt, the ocean will rise to the 20th story of tall buildings? [*see top illustration at left*]. The search for traces of early man far out on the shelf began with the discovery of what may be the remains of an oyster dinner on a former beach off Chesapeake Bay, a site that is now 43 meters below sea level. This discovery was made from the Woods Hole Oceanographic Institution's research submarine *Alvin;* many similar discoveries will probably be made during the next decade.

Submerged barrier beaches are common on the continental shelf, but they are easily confused with the sand waves that are formed by strong currents. More spectacular and of certain origin are the submerged sea cliffs and terraces that mark the temporary stillstands of the sea level. Most of the shelves that have been studied have four to six such terraces, but the recognition of the terraces depends on their width and sharpness. On gently sloping shelves the terraces are almost imperceptible; on steep shelves they are narrow or absent; on shelves receiving a large supply of sediment they are buried. Variation in depth is to be expected in view of the large variation in depth of the most prominent terrace of all—the edge of the shelf. Passing through the terraces are channels cut by streams that flowed across the shelf when the sea level was low. Most of these channels have been filled by sediment; they can be recognized only by seismic profiling and by drilling on the shore at the mouths of stream valleys. Probably hundreds of channels cross the continental shelves of the U.S., but only a dozen are known. One channel, the one cut by the Hudson River off New York, is so large it is not yet filled with sediment.

At the seaward end of the channels, near the edge of the shelf, the channels are replaced by the heads of submarine canyons that continue down the continental slope to depths of several kilometers. The continuation of the submarine canyons to depths far below the maximum probable lowering of the sea level means that the canyons must have been formed by some process that operates under the ocean surface. Although the matter is still the subject of debate, most of the evidence favors the view that the canyons were excavated by turbidity

currents: currents that arise when sediment slips down a slope and becomes mixed with overlying water, thereby increasing its density so that it continues down the slope, often at high speed. Today the shelf off the East Coast of the U.S. is only slightly modified by submarine canyons; only the heads of the canyons indent the shelf edge. When the sea level was at its lowest, the canyons were probably important factors in sedimentation. The shelf off the West Coast of the U.S. is so narrow that the heads of many canyons reach almost to the shore. In those areas the canyons serve to trap and divert sand that is moved along in the shore zone under the influence of wind-driven waves and their associated currents. As a result the sand that is brought to the shore by streams and cliff erosion is only temporarily added to the beaches; eventually it moves seaward through the canyons in the form of slow sand glaciers or rapid turbidity currents.

The water above the continental shelves is complex in composition and movement because it is shallow and

close to the land. Large rivers contribute so much fresh water that they dilute the ocean, but they also increase the local concentration of calcium, phosphate, silica and nitrate—precisely those elements and compounds that elsewhere in the ocean have been reduced to low concentration by incorporation into marine plants and animals. Continental-shelf waters that are distant from river mouths are sometimes saltier than the open sea because their rate of evaporation is high. Local variations in salinity (and therefore density) control the direction of currents on the shelf. For example, the low salinity at the mouth of a river means a higher sea level near the shore than farther out on the shelf, leading to a flow toward the right (when one is facing the ocean in the Northern Hemisphere).

Just at the shore, however, the longshore currents are mainly controlled by the angle at which waves intersect the beach, which in turn is a function of the wind direction. As a result the cur-

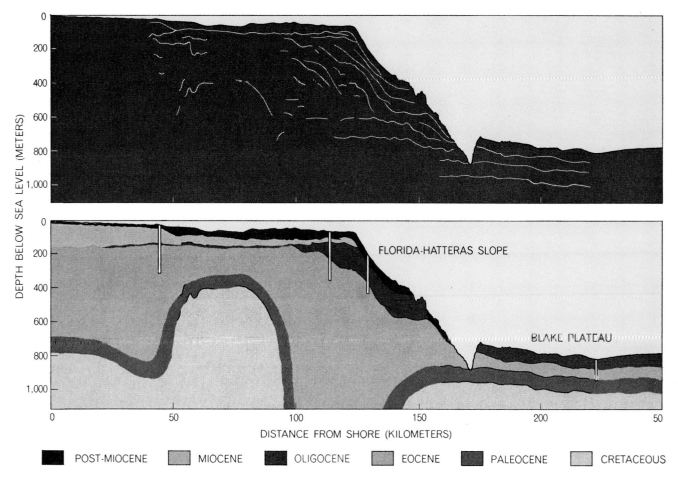

SHELF OFF JACKSONVILLE, FLA., has been studied by two geophysical methods: seismic reflection (*top*) and drilling (*bottom*). Seismic studies can show only the general nature of the stratigraphy. Cores obtained by the JOIDES project, a drilling study conducted by a consortium of institutions, made it possible to map the stratigraphy in considerable detail. The vertical scale is exaggerated 67 times. The approximate termination dates for the various geologic periods are as follows: Miocene, 10 million years ago; Oligocene, 25 million years ago; Eocene, 40 million years ago; Paleocene, 55 million years ago; Cretaceous, 65 million years ago.

rent in the wave zone may be northward, the current on the inner half of the shelf may be southward and the current on the outer shelf may be northward again (for example where an oceanic current such as the Gulf Stream runs along the edge of the shelf). Where rivers bring water to the ocean there must be a gen-

eral current component toward the ocean at the surface; this induces a return flow toward the land at the bottom [see top illustration on page 51]. Thus the sediment on the sea floor may be moved landward, often working its way into the mouths of estuaries. This means estuaries are truly ephemeral features, re-

ceiving sediments from both rivers and the open shelf.

Temperature zones on land are mainly a function of latitude, with secondary modifications resulting from winds whose direction may change seasonally or may be controlled by topography. Similarly, ocean water is cooled at high

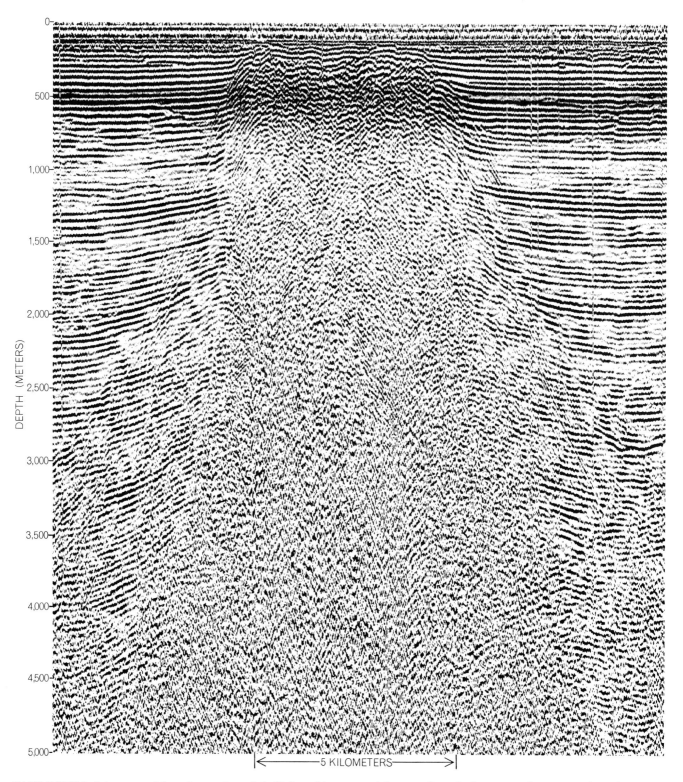

SALT DOME bulging upward into the continental shelf about 10 miles south of Galveston in the Gulf of Mexico is shown in this seismic record. The water is so shallow (between 10 and 20 meters) that the reflection from the surface of the shelf is virtually at the

top of the recording. Geologists can discern significant features in such a record down to a depth of about 3,000 meters. The record was made by the Teledyne Exploration Company. The salt dome was subsequently drilled and was found to contain hydrocarbons.

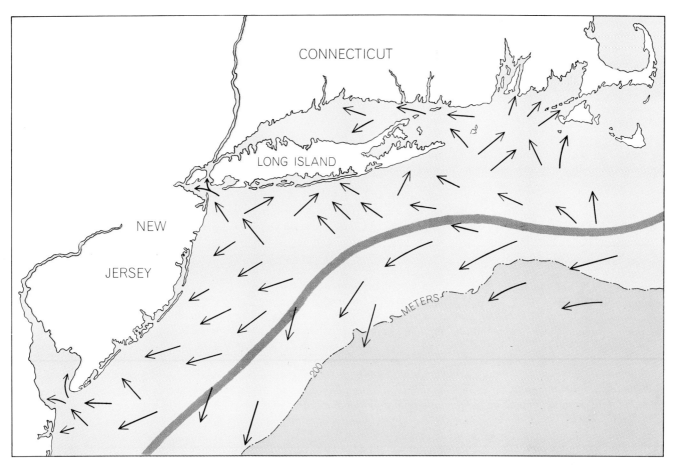

BOTTOM CURRENTS, indicated by arrows, can be traced with the help of simple plastic devices called bottom-drifters. The gray band marks the boundary between landward flow and seaward flow. The broken line represents the edge of the continental shelf.

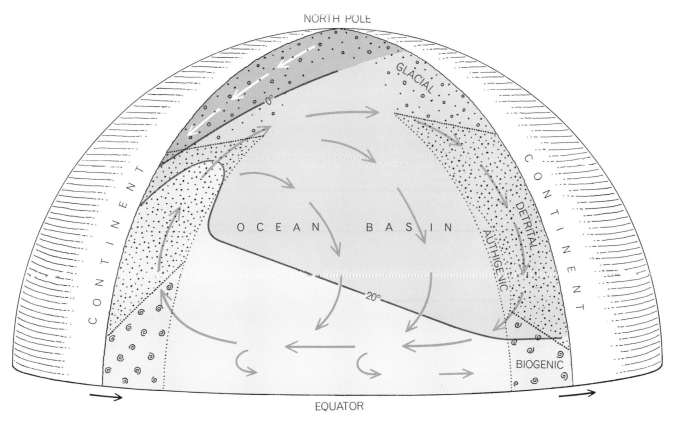

CHARACTER OF SHELF SEDIMENTS around an ocean basin, shown here schematically, is heavily influenced by oceanic currents. The rotation of the earth produces a clockwise flow in the Northern Hemisphere, so that the western edge of the basin, up to a certain latitude, is warmer than the eastern edge. Thus biogenic sediments extend farther north on the west than on the east. The effect would be greater except for a counterflow of arctic water on the western side of the basin. Detrital sediments are the typical outwash of continents. Authigenic sediments are minerals that come out of solution under suitable conditions and fall to the ocean floor.

latitudes and heated at low ones. At the same time, however, the pattern of currents in the open ocean displaces the climatic zones in a clockwise direction in the Northern Hemisphere and counterclockwise in the Southern Hemisphere. The displacement causes the water above the shelf at middle latitudes to be warmer on the western side of an ocean than on the eastern side [see the bottom illustration on page 51]. At high latitudes the flow of arctic water makes the shelf colder on the western side than on the eastern one. As a result the correlation of animal species with shelf latitude shows a displacement on the opposite sides of oceans. Moreover, temperature zones are compressed on the western side and expanded on the eastern. The movements of currents, waves and tides above the shelves are so complex that they have received little study compared with those of the deep ocean. Much fieldwork is needed.

The present great interest in exploring the world's continental shelves flows from their potential economic exploitation. About 90 percent of the world's marine food resources, now extracted at the rate of $8 billion per year, comes from the shelves and adjacent bays [see "The Food Resources of the Ocean," by S. J. Holt, page 93]. Most of this is fish for human and animal consumption; the remainder is largely used for fertilizer.

Second in economic importance is petroleum and natural gas from the shelf; their present annual value is about $4 billion, representing nearly a fifth of the total world production of these substances [see "The Physical Resources of the Ocean," by Edward Wenk, Jr., page 81]. Currently about $1 billion worth of oil and gas a year is extracted from the shelves off the U.S., and much of the rest was developed by American companies with interests abroad. It is safe to predict that the future production from the world's continental shelves will increase at a greater rate than production from wells drilled on land.

The third marine resource in terms of present annual production and future potential is lowly sand and gravel. At present about $200 million worth per year is mined for landfill and road construction in the U.S., for concrete aggregate in Britain and for both purposes elsewhere. As cities and megalopolises continue to grow and show a preference for the coastal regions, and as readily available stream deposits are exhausted or are overlain by houses, there is every prospect that the offshore production of sand and gravel will increase greatly.

We read much about the possibility of economic exploitation of valuable heavy minerals from the sea floor, namely ilmenite, rutile, zircon, tin, monazite, iron, gold and diamonds. The total production of these minerals from below the sea is now less than $50 million per year. Production may increase, particularly in the case of tin, but it is decreasing for iron. Prospects for gold are not very hopeful, and diamonds have never been mined profitably from the sea floor. The basic problem is that economic placer deposits of tin and gold are found only within a few kilometers of the original igneous sources, and few continental shelves contain metalliferous igneous sources. Similarly, ilmenite, rutile, zircon and monazite require the high-energy wave environment of beaches to form deposits that are concentrated enough and large enough to be mined at a profit.

When ancient beach deposits are submerged, even if they are not buried under worthless sediment or mixed with it, the cost of mining increases substantially. They will probably be mined in the future but not until they are economically competitive with shoreline deposits. This could come about either through a rise in prices, resulting from a diminution of known deposits on land, or when more efficient mining and separation methods are devised for the marine environment.

Phosphorite is present in large quantities on shelves off southern California, Peru, southeastern Africa, northeastern Africa and Florida. It can be mined off the U.S., but it has to compete with high-grade land deposits in Florida, Montana, Idaho and Wyoming (where there is about a 1,000-year supply at present rates of mining). Most investigators have concluded that the cost of mining at sea exceeds the cost of mining on land plus the costs of land transportation. Some deposits far from the U.S., however, may justify mining, particularly because some of them may be near places where there is a great need for fertilizer, such as India. Unfortunately the distribution of phosphorite in these areas is poorly known, and little or no effort is currently being expended on their investigation.

The would-be exploiter of the ocean will do well to remember the words of the old Newfoundland skipper, "We don't be *takin'* nothin' from the sea. We has to sneak up on what we wants and wiggle it away." Nevertheless, the continental shelves, when they are properly investigated, promise to greatly increase our knowledge of the earth's history and to become a steadily more important source of food and raw materials.

V

The Deep-Ocean Floor

The Deep-Ocean Floor

H. W. MENARD

The discovery that it is growing outward from the mid-ocean ridges has suggested that it is formed in huge plates that act as units in the dynamic processes of the earth's crust

Oceanic geology is in the midst of a revolution. All the data gathered over the past 30 years—the soundings of the deep ocean, the samples and photographs of the bottom, the measurements of heat flow and magnetism—are being reinterpreted according to the concept of continental drift and two new concepts: sea-floor spreading and plate tectonics (the notion that the earth's crust consists of plates that are created at one edge and destroyed at the other). Discoveries are made and interpretations developed so often that the scientific literature cannot keep up with them; they are reported by preprint and wandering minstrel. At such a time any broad synthesis is likely to be short-lived, yet so many diverse observations can now be fitted into a coherent picture that it seems worthwhile to present it.

Before continental drift, sea-floor spreading and plate tectonics captured the imagination of geologists, most of them conceived the earth's crust as being a fairly stable layer enveloping the earth's fluid mantle and core. The only kind of motion normally perceived in this picture was isostasy: the tendency of crustal blocks to float on a plastic mantle. The horizontal displacement of any geologic feature by as much as 100 kilometers was considered startling. This

PILLOW LAVA assumes its rounded shape because it cools rapidly in ocean water. This flow lies on the western slope of the mid-ocean ridge in the South Atlantic at a depth of 2,650 meters. Such flows erupt from the many volcanic vents and fissures that are created as the ocean floor spreads out from the mid-ocean ridges in the form of vast crustal plates. The photograph was made under the direction of Maurice Ewing of the Lamont-Doherty Geological Observatory.

view is no longer consistent with the geological evidence. Instead each new discovery seems to favor sea-floor spreading, continental drift and plate tectonics. These concepts are described elsewhere in this issue [see "The Origin of the Oceans," by Sir Edward Bullard, page 15]. Here I shall recapitulate them briefly to show how they are related to the actual features of the deep-ocean floor.

According to plate tectonics the earth's crust is divided into huge segments afloat on the mantle. When such a plate is in motion on the sphere of the earth, it describes a circle around a point termed the pole of rotation (not to be confused with the entire earth's pole of rotation). This motion has profound geological effects. When two plates move apart, a fissure called a spreading center opens between them. Through this fissure rises the hot, plastic material of the mantle, which solidifies and joins the trailing edge of each plate. Meanwhile the edge of the plate farthest from the spreading center—the leading edge—pushes against another plate. Where that happens, the leading edge may be deflected downward so that it sinks into a region of soft material called the asthenosphere, 100 kilometers or more below the surface. This process destroys the plate material at the same rate at which it is being created at its trailing edge. Many of the fissures where plate material is being created are in the middle of the ocean floor, which therefore spreads continuously from a median line. Where the plates float apart, the continents, which are embedded in them, also drift away from one another.

The most obvious consequence of this process on the ocean floor is the symmetrical seascape on each side of a spreading center. As two crustal plates

move apart (at a rate of one to 10 centimeters per year), the basaltic material that wells up through the spreading center between them splits down the middle. The upwelling in some way produces a ridge, flanked on each side by deep ocean basins and capped by long hills and mountains that run parallel to the crest. The flow of heat from the earth's interior is generally high along the crest because dikes of molten rock have been injected at the spreading center. A spreading center may also open under a continent. If it does, it produces a linear deep such as the Red Sea or the Gulf of California. If it continues to spread, or if the spreading center opens in an existing ocean basin, the same symmetrical seascape is ultimately formed.

This symmetry extends to less tangible features of the ocean floor such as the magnetic patterns in the basalt of the slopes on either side of the mid-ocean ridge. As the plastic material reaches the surface and hardens, it "freezes" into it the direction of the earth's magnetic field. The earth's magnetic field reverses from time to time, and as each band of new material moves outward across the ocean floor it retains a magnetic pattern shared by a corresponding band on the other side of the ridge. The result is a matching set of parallel bands on both sides. These patterns provide evidence of symmetrical flows and make it possible to date them, since they correspond to similar patterns on land that have been reliably dated by other means.

The steepness of the mid-ocean ridge is determined by a balance between the rate at which material moves outward from the spreading center and the rate at which it sinks as it ages after solidifying. The rate of sinking remains fairly constant throughout the ocean basin, and it seems to depend on the age of the

55

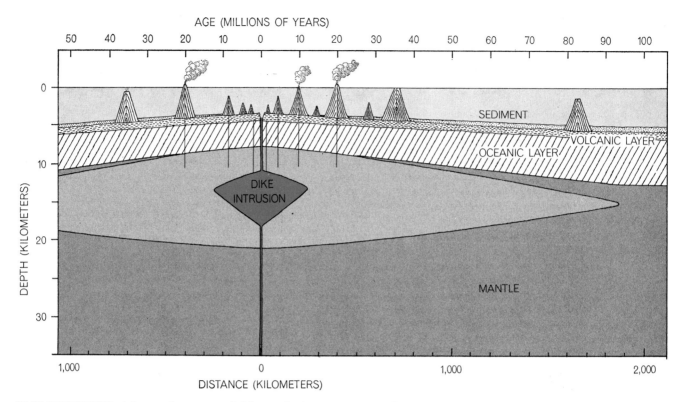

FAST SPREADING of the sea floor is revealed by gentle slopes. The sea floor is created at a spreading center that leaks molten rock from several dikes intruding from a pool in the low-density mantle (*light shading*). As the molten rock emerges it cools and adheres to the crust sliding away on each side of the fissure. If the crust moves at more than three centimeters per year, the slopes are gradual because spreading, which is horizontal, is rapid compared with the sinking of the crust. The balance between the two determines the steepness of the slope. Fast spreading also produces a thin volcanic layer because material moves so quickly from the fissure that it cannot accumulate. Islands built by eruptions are distant from the center because they grow on rapidly moving crust.

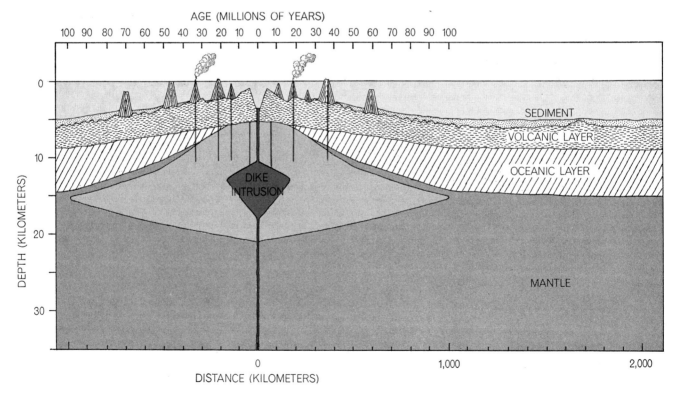

SLOW SPREADING produces steep slopes. Here the crust moves less than three centimeters per year; consequently sinking dominates the slope-forming process and produces steep escarpments. The volcanic layer is thicker at a slow center because material has time to accumulate. Mountains and volcanoes are high near the spreading center because the crust moves so slowly that the lava piles up. After 100 million years crust produced from a slow spreading center has strong similarity to crust from a fast center. Both kinds of crust have sunk to a depth of five kilometers. The oceanic layer is about five kilometers thick. Both fast- and slow-spreading crust are covered by the same kind of sediment. Slow spreading occurs mainly in the Atlantic, fast spreading in the Pacific.

crust. It can be calculated if the age of the oceanic crust (as indicated by the magnetic patterns) is divided into the depth at which a particular section lies. Such calculations show that the crust sinks about nine centimeters per 1,000 years for the first 10 million years after it forms, 3.3 centimeters per 1,000 years for the next 30 million years, and two centimeters per 1,000 years thereafter. Not all the crust sinks: on the southern Mid-Atlantic Ridge the sea floor has remained at the same level for as long as 20 million years.

The rate at which the sea floor spreads varies from one to 10 centimeters per year. Therefore fast spreading builds broad elevations and gentle slopes such as those of the East Pacific Rise. The steep, concave flanks of the Mid-Atlantic Ridge, on the other hand, were formed by slow spreading.

Whether the slopes are steep or gentle, the trailing edge of the plate at the spreading center is about three kilometers higher than the leading edge on the other side of the plate. The reason for this difference in elevation is not known. Heating causes some elevation and cooling some sinking, but the total relief appears much too great to be attributed to thermal expansion. Cooling might account for the relatively rapid sinking observed during the first 10 million years, but continued sinking remains a puzzle.

A decade ago scanty information suggested that the mid-ocean ridge in both the Atlantic and Pacific was continuous, with a few branches. More complete surveys have revealed that crustal plates have ragged edges. Instead of extending unbroken for thousands of kilometers, a mid-ocean ridge at the trailing edges of two crustal plates forms a zigzag line consisting of many short segments connected by fracture zones to other ridges, trenches, young mountain ranges or crustal sinks. The fracture zones connecting the ridge segments are associated with what are called "transform" faults. They provide important clues to the history of a plate. Because they form some of the edges of the plate, they delineate the circle around its pole of rotation, thereby indicating the direction in which it has been moving.

From what has been said so far it might appear that the spreading centers are fixed and stationary. The constantly repeated splitting of the new crust at the spreading center produces symmetrical continental margins, symmetrical magnetic patterns on the ocean floor, symmetrical ridge flanks and even

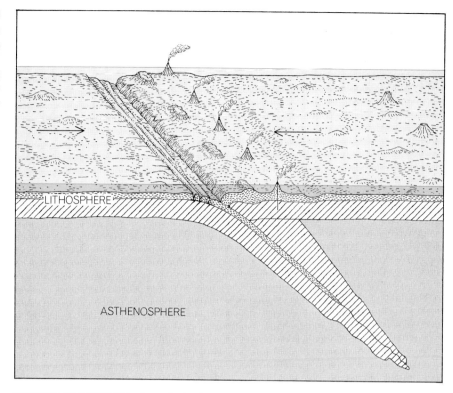

TRENCH IS CREATED where the leading edge of a plate that emerges from a fast spreading center collides with another plate. Because the combined speed of the two is more than six centimeters per year neither can absorb the impact by buckling. Instead one crustal plate (*in lithosphere*) plunges under the other to be destroyed in the asthenosphere, a hot, weak layer below. The impact produces volcanoes, islands and a deep, such as the Tonga Trench. Beside a trench are cracks that are produced by bending of the crust.

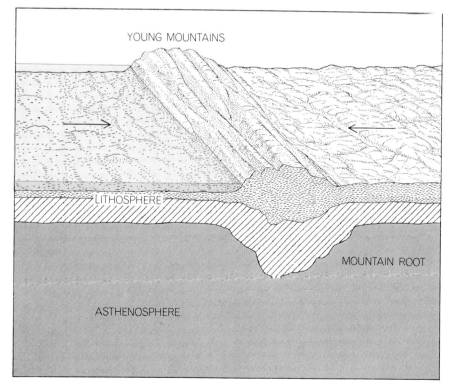

MOUNTAIN RANGE IS FORMED when the leading edges of two plates come together at less than six centimeters per year. Instead of colliding catastrophically, so that one plate slides under the other, both plates buckle, raising a young mountain range between them. The range consists of crustal material that folds upward under the compression exerted by the two plates (and also downward, forming the root of the mountain). Such ranges can be identified because they contain cherts and other material typical of the ocean bottom.

symmetrical mountain ranges. More often than not, however, it has been found that the spreading center itself moves. Oddly enough such movement gives rise to the same symmetrical geology. All that is required in order to maintain the symmetry is that the spreading center move at exactly half the rate at which the plates are separating. If it moved faster or slower, the symmetry of the magnetic patterns would be destroyed.

Imagine, for instance, that the plate to the east of a spreading center remains stationary as the plate to the west moves. Since the material welling up through the fissure splits down the middle, half of it adheres to the stationary plate and the other half adheres to the moving plate. The next flow of material to well up through the split thus appears half

the width of the spreading center away from the stationary plate. The flow after that appears a whole width of the spreading center away from the stationary plate, and so on. In effect the spreading center is migrating away from the stationary plate and following the moving one. If the speed of the spreading center exceeded half the speed of the migrating plate, however, a kind of geological Doppler effect would set in: the bands of the magnetic pattern would be condensed in the direction of the moving plate, and they would be stretched out in the direction of the stationary plate [see illustration below].

It might seem unlikely that the spreading center would maintain its even rate of speed and remain exactly between the two plates. W. Jason Morgan of Princeton University observes, how-

ever, that there is no impediment to such motion, provided only that the crust splits where it is weakest (which is where it split before, at the point where the hot dike was originally injected). As a result the spreading center is always exactly between two crustal plates whether it moves or not.

Moving spreading centers account for some of the major features of the ocean floor. The Chile Rise off the coast of South America and the East Pacific Rise are adjacent spreading centers. Since there is no crustal sink between them, and new plate is constantly being added on the inside edge of each rise, at least one of the centers must be moving, otherwise the basin between them might fold and thrust upward into a mountain range or downward into a trench. Similarly, the Carlsberg Ridge in the Indian Ocean and the Mid-Atlantic Ridge are not separated by a crustal sink and hence one of them must be moving.

A moving center may have created the ancient Darwin Rise on the western edge of the Pacific basin and also the modern East Pacific Rise. As in the case of the Carlsberg Ridge and the Mid-Atlantic Ridge, the existence of two vast spreading centers on opposite sides of the ocean with no intervening crustal sink has puzzled geologists. If such centers can move, however, it is possible that the spreading center in the western Pacific merely migrated all the way across the basin, leaving behind the ridges of the Darwin Rise. In this way one rise could simply have become the other. Many other examples exist, and Manik Talwani of the Lamont-Doherty Geological Observatory proposes that all spreading centers move.

As a plate forms at a spreading center it consists of two layers of material, an upper "volcanic" layer and a lower "oceanic" one. Lava and feeder dikes from the mantle form the volcanic layer; its rocks are oceanic tholeiite (or a metamorphosed equivalent), which is rich in aluminum and poor in potassium. The oceanic layer is also some form of mantle material, but its precise composition, density and condition are not known. Farther down the slope of the ridge the plate acquires a third layer consisting of sediment.

The sediment comes from the continents and sifts down on all parts of the basin, accumulating to a considerable depth. It is mixed with a residue of the hard parts of microorganisms that is called calcareous ooze. Below a certain depth (which varies among regions) this

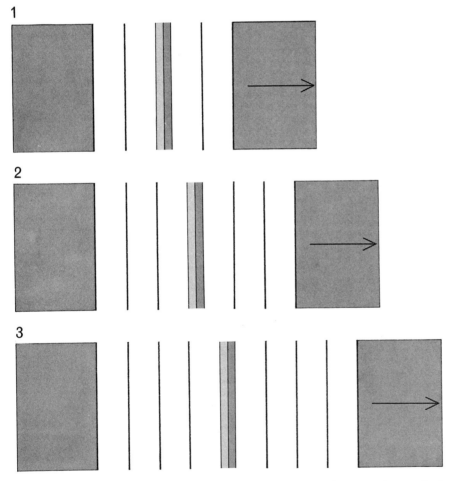

1

2

3

SPREADING CENTER MOVES, yet it can still leave a symmetrical pattern of magnetized rock. The molten material emerging from a spreading center becomes magnetized because as it cools it captures the prevailing direction of the earth's periodically changing magnetic field. In the instance illustrated here the right-hand plate moves out to the right while the left-hand plate remains stationary. In 1 hot material from a dike arrives at the surface, cools and splits down the middle. In 2 the next injection of material arrives in the crevice between the two halves of the preceding mass of rock. The new mass is therefore half the width of the preceding mass farther from the stationary plate than the preceding mass of material itself was. In 3 the new material has cooled and split in its turn and another mass has appeared that is a whole width farther from the left-hand plate. As long as the center moves at half the speed at which the right-hand plate moves away the magnetic bands remain symmetrical. If plate moved faster or more slowly, they would be jumbled.

material dissolves, and only red clay and other resistant components remain.

For reasons only partly known the sediment is not uniformly distributed. At the spreading center the newly created crust is of course bare of sediment, and within 100 kilometers of such a center the calcareous ooze is rarely thick enough to measure. The ooze accumulates at an average rate of 10 meters for each million years, during which time the plate moves horizontally from 10,000 to 100,000 meters and sinks 100 meters. Where the red clay appears, it accumulates at a rate of less than one meter per million years.

The puzzle deepens when one considers that sediment on oceanic crust older than 20 million years stops increasing in thickness after it sinks to the depth where the calcareous ooze dissolves. Indeed, in many places the age of the oldest sediment is about the same as the volcanic layer on which it lies. It would therefore seem that almost all the deep-ocean sediment accumulates in narrow zones on the flanks of the mid-ocean ridges. If this is correct, it has yet to be explained.

The volcanic layer forms mainly at the spreading center. Volcanoes and vents on the slopes of the mid-ocean ridge contribute a certain amount of oceanic tholeiite to it. It can be said in general that the thickness of the volcanic layer decreases as the spreading rate increases. If the crust spreads slowly, the material has time to accumulate. Fast spreading reduces this time and therefore the accumulation. The conclusion can be drawn that the rate at which the volcanic-layer material is discharged is nearly constant. These relations are based on only 10 observations, but they apply to spreading rates from 1.4 centimeters to 12 centimeters per year, and to thicknesses from .8 kilometer to 3.8 kilometers.

The total flow of volcanic material from all active spreading centers is about four cubic kilometers per year—four times the flow on the continents. Not the slightest sign of this volcanism on the ocean bottom can be detected at the surface of the ocean, with one possible exception: late in the 19th century a ship reported seeing smoke rising from the waters above the equatorial Mid-Atlantic Ridge. The British oceanographer Sir John Murray remarked that he hoped the smoke signified the emergence of an island, since the Royal Navy needed a coaling station at that point.

Like the volcanic layer, the oceanic

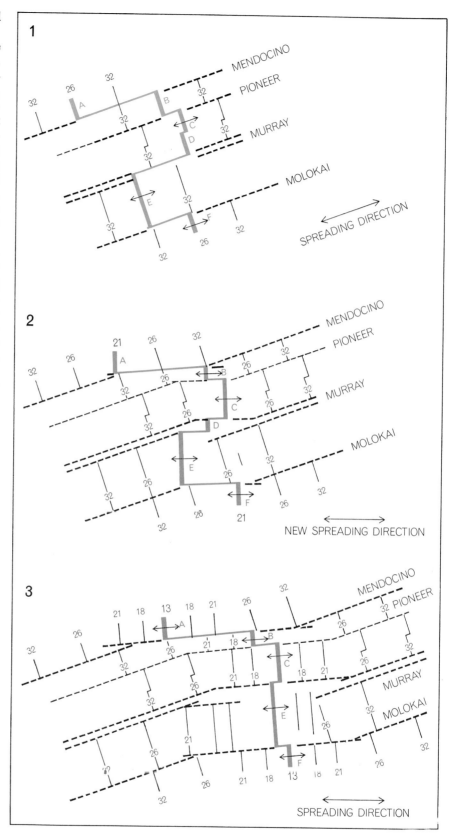

HOW A PLATE MOVES is revealed by the patterns of magnetic bands (time of formation is indicated by numbers) and by the relation between ridges and faults in the northeastern Pacific. At the time illustrated in *1* material from the Murray fault and other faults connected segments of the ridge (*indicated by letters*) offset from one another by plate motion. At the time shown in *2* the spreading direction changed. The readjustment of the plates has shortened the Pioneer-Mendocino ridge segment (*B*) while lengthening and reorienting the Pioneer, Mendocino and Molokai transform faults. In *3* the Mendocino fault remains the same length, but between most of the other ridges faults have been shortened or have almost disappeared as ridge segments tended to rejoin one another. Between Murray and Molokai faults ridge has jumped eastward, and one segment (*D*) has vanished.

layer forms at the spreading center. Acoustical measurements of the thickness of this layer at spreading centers, on the flanks of mid-ocean ridges and on the deep-ocean floor show, however, that at least part of the oceanic layer evolves slowly from the mantle rather than solidifying quickly and completely at the spreading center. At the spreading center the thickness of the layer depends on how fast the ocean floor moves. In regions such as the South Atlantic, where the floor spreads at a rate of two centimeters per year, no oceanic layer forms within a few hundred kilometers of the spreading center. Farther away from the spreading center the oceanic layer accumulates rapidly, reaching a normal thickness of four to five kilometers on the flank of the mid-ocean ridge. A spreading rate of three centimeters per year is associated with an oceanic layer roughly two kilometers deep at the center that thickens by one kilometer in 13 million years. A plate with a spreading rate of eight centimeters per year is three kilometers deep at the center and thickens by one kilometer in 20 million years. Thus the thinner the initial crust is, the faster the thickness increases as the crust spreads.

As a plate flows continuously from the spreading center, faulting, volcanic eruptions and lava flows along the length of the mid-ocean ridge build its mountains and escarpments. This process can be most easily observed in Iceland, a part of the Mid-Atlantic Ridge that has grown so rapidly it has emerged from the ocean. A central rift, 45 kilometers wide at its northern end, cuts the island parallel to the ridge. The sides of the rift consist of active, steplike faults. There are other step faults on the rift floor, which is otherwise dominated by a large number of longitudinal fissures. Some of these fissures are open and filled with dikes. Fluid lava wells up from the fissures and either buries the surrounding mountains, valleys and faults or forms long, low "shield" volcanoes. Two hundred such young volcanoes, which have been erupting about once every five years over the past 1,000 years, dot the floor of the rift. Thirty of them are currently active.

Just as a balance between spreading and sinking shapes the slopes of the mid-ocean ridges, so does a balance between lava discharge and spreading build undersea mountains, hills and valleys. High mountains normally form at slow centers where spreading proceeds at two to 3.5 centimeters per year. In contrast, a spreading center that opens at a rate of five to 12 centimeters per year produces long hills less than 500 meters high. This relationship is a natural consequence of the long-term constancy of the lava discharge. Over a short period of time, however, the lava discharge may fluctuate or pulsate, a picture suggested by the fact that the thick volcanic layer associated with slow spreading can consist of volcanic mountains (which represent copious flow) separated by valleys covered by a thinner volcanic layer.

The volcanic activity and faulting that first appear near the spreading centers decrease rapidly as the plate ages and material moves toward its center, but volcanic activity in some form is never entirely absent. Small conical volcanoes are found on crust only a few hundred thousand years old near spreading centers, and active circular volcanoes such as those of Hawaii exist even in the middle of a plate. It would appear that the great cracks that serve as conduits for dikes and lava flows are soon sealed as a plate ages and spreads. Volcanic activity is then concentrated in a few central vents, created at different times and places.

Many of these vents remain open for tens of millions of years, judging by the size and distribution of the different classes of marine volcanoes. First, the biggest volcanoes are increasingly big at greater distances from a spreading center, which means they must continue to erupt and grow as the crust ages and sinks, even when the age of the crust exceeds 10 million years. In most places, in fact, a volcano needs at least 10 million years in order to grow large enough to become an island. Volcanoes that discharge lava at a rate lower than 100 cubic kilometers per million years never become islands because the sea floor sinks too fast for them to reach the sea surface.

Other volcanoes drifting with a spreading ocean floor may remain active or become active on crust that is 100 million years old (as the volcanoes of the Canary Islands have). Normally, however, volcanoes become inactive by the time the crust is 20 to 30 million years old. This is demonstrated by the existence of guyots, drowned ancient island volcanoes that were submerged by the gradual sinking of the aging crust. Guyots are found almost entirely on crust that is more than 30 million years old, such as the floor of the western equatorial Pacific.

Traditionally it has been thought that marine volcanoes spew lava from a magma chamber located deep in the mantle. Some volcanoes have a top composed of alkali basalt, slopes with transitional basalt outcrops and a base of oceanic tholeiite, and it was therefore assumed that the lava in the magma chamber became differentiated into components that, rather like a pousse-café, separated into several layers of different kinds of material, each of which followed

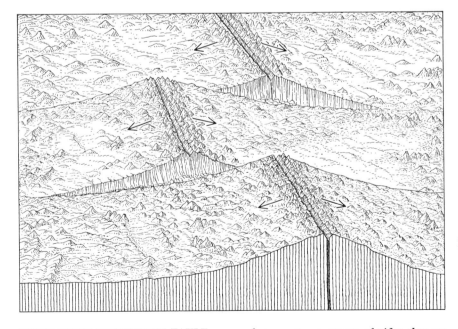

RIDGE-RIDGE TRANSFORM FAULT appears between two segments of ridge that are displaced from each other. Mountains are built, earthquakes shake the plate edges and volcanoes erupt in such an area because of the forces generated as plates, formed at the spreading centers under the ridges, slide past each other in opposite directions. On outer slopes of the mid-ocean ridges, however, this intense seismic activity appears to subside.

the layer above it up the spout. The emergence of plate tectonics and continental drift as respectable concepts have now brought this view of volcanic action into question.

It remains perfectly possible for a volcano to drift for tens of millions of years over hundreds of kilometers while tapping a single magma chamber embedded deep in the mantle. The motion of the plates, however, suggests another hypothesis. According to this view, the volcano and its conduit drift along with the crust as the conduit continually taps different parts of a relatively stationary magma that is ready to yield various kinds of lava whenever a conduit appears. In actuality the composition of the lava usually changes only slightly after the first 10 to 20 kilometers of drifting. Although the older hypothesis is still reasonable, the newer one must also be considered because it explains the facts equally well.

In addition to their characteristic volcanoes and mountains, spreading centers are marked by median valleys, which in places such as the North Atlantic or the northwestern Indian Ocean are deeper than the surrounding region. These rifts are commonly found in centers opening at a rate of two to five centimeters per year. The deepest rifts, which may go as deep as 1,000 to 1,300 meters below the surrounding floor, are associated with spreading at three to four centimeters per year. Only one valley is known to be associated with spreading at five to 12 centimeters per year. Although rifts are not found in all spreading centers, they usually do appear in conjunction with a slow center. Both of these features are also associated with volcanic activity.

The mid-ocean ridges, as we have noted, seldom run unbroken for more than a few hundred kilometers. They are interrupted by fracture zones, and the

segments are shifted out of line with respect to one another. These fracture zones run at right angles to the ridge and connect the segments. Where they lie between the segments they are termed ridge-ridge transform faults, which are the site of intense geological activity. As the two edges of the fault slide past each other they rub and produce earthquakes. The slope of a transform fault drops steeply from the crest of one ridge segment to a point halfway between it and the adjacent segment and then climbs to the top of the adjacent segment, reflecting the fact that the crust is elevated at the spreading center and subsides at some distance from it [*see illustration on page 60*].

Like spreading centers, fracture zones have their own complex geology. In these areas the ridges stand as much as several kilometers high, and the troughs are equally deep. It appears that the same volcanic forces that shape the main

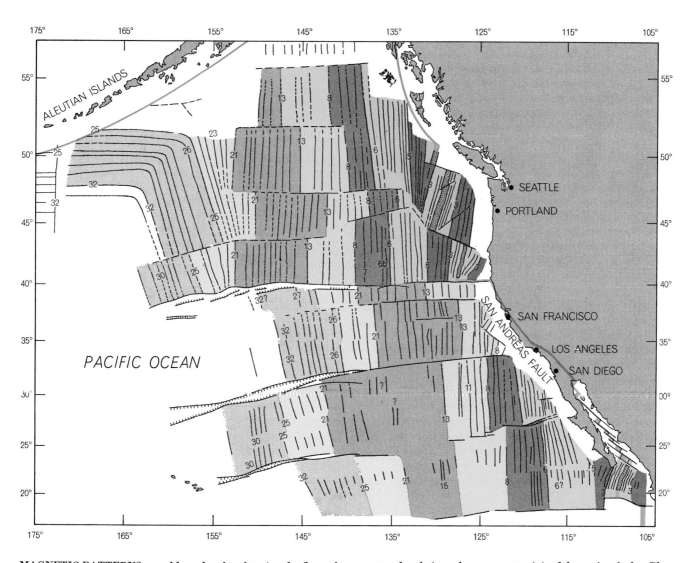

MAGNETIC PATTERNS reveal how the plate forming the floor of the northeastern Pacific has moved. Its active eastern edge now stretches from Alaska through California (where it forms the San Andreas fault) to the Gulf of California. In the gulf spreading centers break into short segments joined by active faults. Plate motion is opening the gulf and moving coastal California in the direction of the Aleutians. To the south lies the Great Magnetic Bight, formed by three plates that spread away from one another.

ridges produce the mountains and valleys of the faults. As fracture zones open they slowly leak lava from hot dikes. At the same time the crust sinks away from the fault line, and this balance produces high mountains.

Beyond the spreading centers the fracture zones become the inactive remains of earlier faulting. The different rates at which these outer flanks of the mid-ocean ridge sink do produce some vertical motion as the scarps of the fracture zone decay. This may account for the few earthquakes in these areas. I should emphasize that it is not known if horizontal motion is also absent from such dead fracture zones. It is not necessary, however, to postulate such motion in order to explain existing observations.

A fracture zone can become active again at any time, but if it does so, it becomes the side of a smaller new plate rather than part of the trailing edge of an old one. If the flank fracture zones are as quiescent as they appear to be, then the plates forming the earth's crust are large and long-lived. If these fracture zones were active, on the other hand, it could only be concluded that each one marked the flank of a small, elongated plate.

The direction the plate is moving can be deduced from the magnetic pattern that runs at right angles to the fractures in the fracture zone. When the direction of plate motion changes, the direction in which the fracture zone moves also changes. This change in direction can be most clearly seen in the northeastern Pacific, where our knowledge is most detailed. On this part of the ocean floor the changes of direction have taken place at the same time in many zones, indicating that the entire North Pacific plate has changed direction as a unit [see illustration on page 61].

On the bottom of the Pacific and the North Atlantic the magnetic patterns are sometimes garbled. Old transform faults may have vanished if short segments of spreading center have been united by reorientation. By the same token new transform faults may have formed if the change in plate motion has been too rapid to be accommodated by existing motions. Thus fracture zones may be discontinuous. They may start and stop abruptly, and the offset of the magnetic patterns may change from place to place along them without indicating any activity except at the former edges of plates.

Some patterns are even harder to interpret. Douglas J. Elvers and his colleagues in the U.S. Coast and Geodetic Survey discovered an abrupt boomerang-shaped bend in the magnetic pattern south of the Aleutians. The arms of this configuration, which Elvers calls the

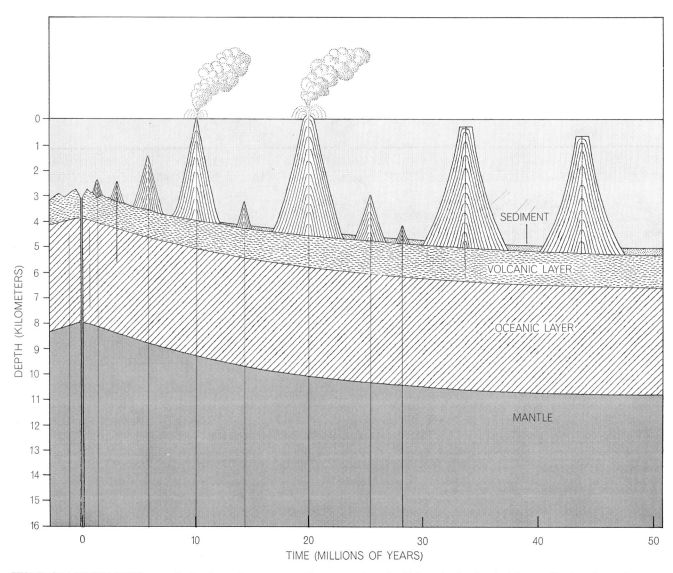

UNDERSEA VOLCANOES normally begin to rise near spreading centers. Then they ride along on the moving plate as they grow. If a volcano rises fast enough to surmount the original depth of the water and the sinking of the ocean floor, it emerges as an island such as St. Helena in the South Atlantic. To rise above the water an undersea volcano must grow to a height of about four kilometers in 10 million years. Island volcanoes sink after 20 to 30 million years and become the sediment-capped seamounts called guyots.

Great Magnetic Bight, are offset by fracture zones at right angles to the magnetic pattern. The Great Magnetic Bight seems to have required impossible forms of sea-floor spreading and plate movement. However, Walter C. Pitman III and Dennis E. Hayes of the Lamont-Doher-

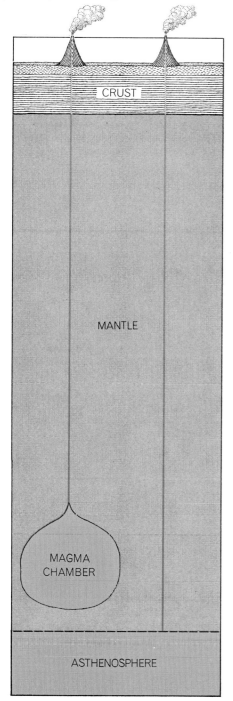

UNDERSEA ERUPTIONS can be explained in two ways, both consistent with observed facts. Since a volcano consists of different kinds of rock, it was originally thought that its conduit carried different forms of lava up from a magma chamber 50 kilometers or more down in the mantle. Now that crustal plates have been found to move, another theory must be considered. According to this idea, the conduit reaches through the mantle and taps several different kinds of magma at different places in the asthenosphere.

ty Geological Observatory, among others, have been able to show that the configuration is fully understandable if it is assumed that the trailing edges of three plates met and formed a Y. Similar complex patterns have now been found in the Atlantic and the Pacific. Indeed, if the transform faults are perpendicular to the spreading centers and two spreading rates are known, both the orientation and the spreading rate of the third spreading center can be calculated even before it is mapped. One can also calculate the orientation and spreading rate for a third center that has already vanished in a trench.

As a crustal plate grows, its leading edge is destroyed at an equal rate. Sometimes this edge slides under the oncoming edge of another plate and returns to the asthenosphere. When this happens, a deep trench such as the Mariana Trench and the Tonga Trench in the Pacific is formed. In other areas the movement of the crust creates young mountain ranges. Xavier Le Pichon of the Lamont-Doherty Geological Observatory concludes that the occurrence of one event or the other is a function of the rate at which plates are moving together. If the rate is less than five to six centimeters per year, the crust can absorb the compression and buckles up into large mountain ranges such as the Himalayas. In these ranges folding and overthrusting deform and shorten the crust. If the rate is higher, the plate breaks free and sinks into the mantle, creating an oceanic trench in which the topography and surface structure indicate tension.

Several crustal sinks are no longer active. Their past, however, can be deduced from their geology. Large-scale folding and thrust-faulting can be taken as evidence of the former presence of a crustal sink, although such deformation can also arise in other ways. Certain types of rock may also indicate the formation of a trench. The arcs of islands that lie parallel to trenches, for instance, are characterized by volcanoes that produce andesitic lavas, which are quite different from the basaltic lavas of the ocean floor. The trenches themselves, and the deep-sea floor in general, are featured by deposits of graywackes and cherts. These rocks are commonly found exposed on land in the thick prisms of sediment that lie in geosynclines: large depressed regions created by horizontal forces resembling those generated by a drifting crustal plate. Thus the presence of some or all of these types of rock may indicate the former existence of a crustal sink. This linking of marine geology at

spreading centers with land geology at crustal sinks is becoming one of the most fruitful aspects of plate tectonics. Still, crustal sinks are by no means as informative about the history of the ocean floor as spreading centers are, because in such sinks much of the evidence of past events is destroyed. Even if the leading edge of a plate was once the side of a plate (or vice versa), there would be no way to tell them apart.

At the boundary between the land and the sea a puzzle presents itself. The sides of an oceanic trench move together at more than five centimeters per year, and it would seem that the sediment sliding into the bottom of the trench should be folded into pronounced ridges and valleys. Yet virtually undeformed sediments have been mapped in trenches by David William Scholl and his colleagues at the U.S. Naval Electronics Laboratory Center. Furthermore, the enormous quantity of deep-ocean sediment that has presumably been swept up to the margins of trenches cannot be detected on sub-bottom profiling records. There are many ingenious (but unpublished) explanations of the phenomenon in terms of plate tectonics. One of them may conceivably be correct. According to that hypothesis, the sediments are intricately folded in such a way that the slopes and walls of trenches cannot be detected by normal survey techniques, which look at the sediments from the ocean surface and along profiles perpendicular to the slopes. This kind of folding could be detected only by trawling a recording instrument across the trench much closer to the bottom or by crossing the slope at an acute angle.

The concepts of sea-floor spreading and plate tectonics allow a quantitative evaluation of the interaction of many important variables in marine geology. By combining empirical observation with theory it is possible not only to explain but also to predict the thickness and age of sediments in a given locality, the scale and orientation of topographic relief, the thickness of various crustal layers, the orientation and offsetting of magnetic patterns, the distribution and depth of drowned ancient islands, the occurrence of trenches and young mountain ranges, the characteristics of earthquakes, and many other previously unrelated and unpredictable phenomena. This revolution in marine geology may take some years to run its course. Ideas are changing, and new puzzles present themselves even as the old ones are solved. The only certainty is that the subject will never be the same again.

VI

The Nature of Oceanic Life

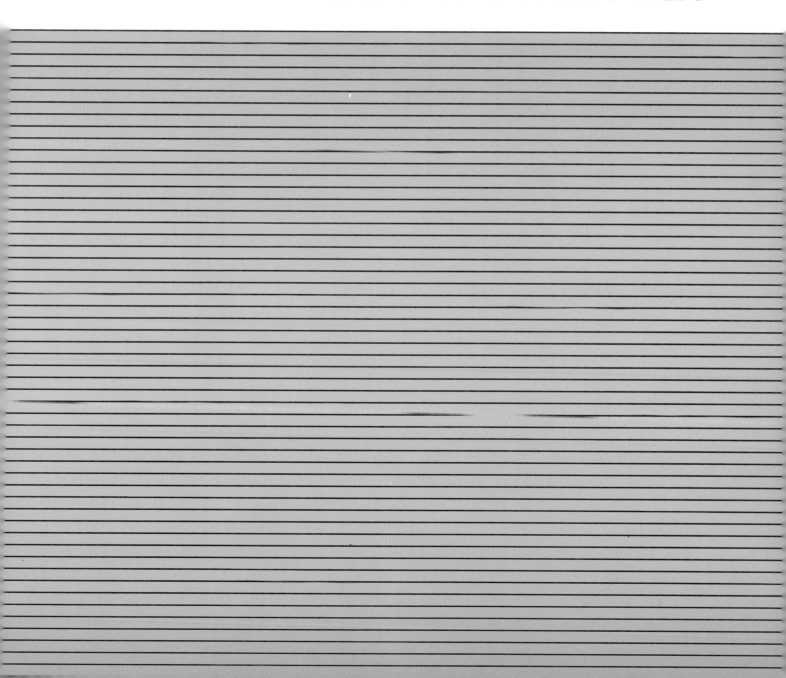

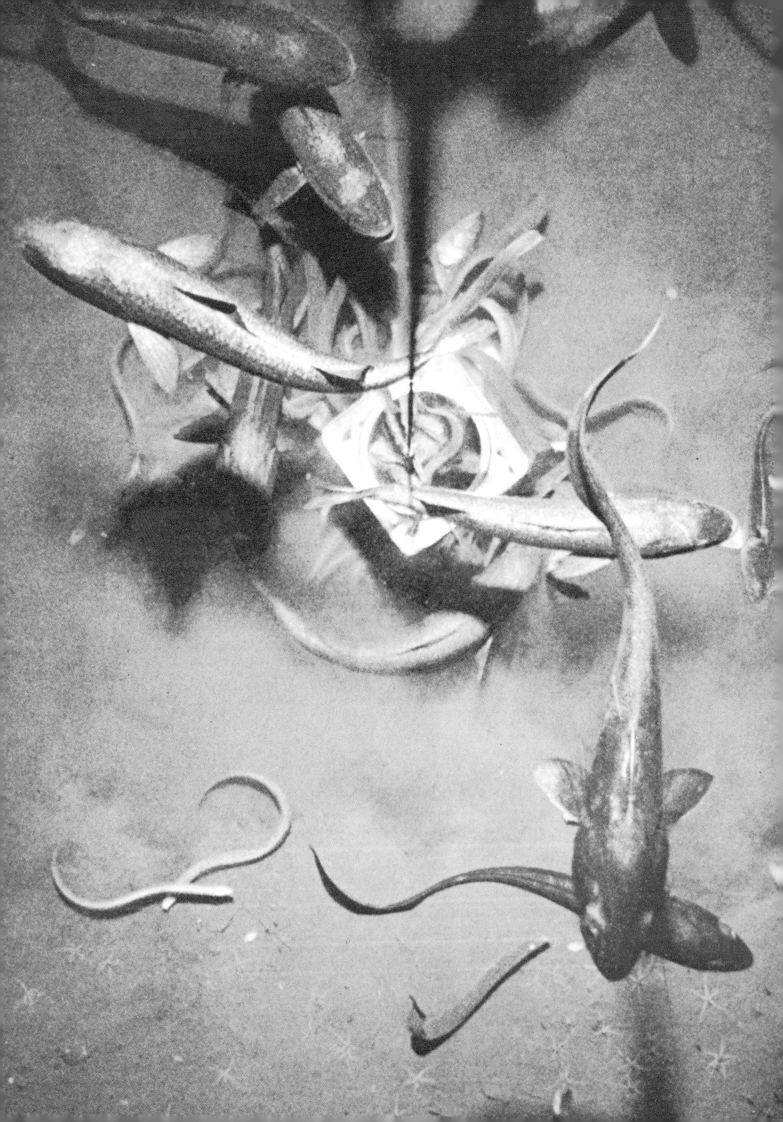

The Nature of Oceanic Life

The conditions of the marine environment have given rise to a food web in which the dominant primary production of organic matter is carried out by microscopic plants

I plan to take the reader on a brief tour of marine life from the surface layers of the open sea, down through the intermediate layers to the deep-sea floor, and from there to the living communities on continental shelves and coral reefs. Like Dante, I shall be able to record only a scattered sampling of the races and inhabitants of each region and to point out only the general dominant factors that typify each domain; in particular I shall review some of the conditions, principles and interactions that appear to have molded the forms of life in the sea and to have established their range and compass.

The organisms of the sea are born, live, breathe, feed, excrete, move, grow, mate, reproduce and die within a single interconnected medium. Thus interactions among the marine organisms and interactions of the organisms with the chemical and physical processes of the sea range across the entire spectrum from simple, adamant constraints to complex effects of many subtle interactions.

Far more, of course, is known about the life of the sea than I shall be able even to suggest, and there are yet to be achieved great steps in our knowledge of the living entities of the sea. I shall mention some of these possibilities in my concluding remarks.

A general discussion of a living system should consider the ways in which plants elaborate basic organic material from inorganic substances and the successive and often highly intricate steps by which organisms then return this material to the inorganic reservoir. The discussion should also show the forms of life by which such processes are conducted. I shall briefly trace these processes through the regions I have indicated, returning later to a more detailed discussion of the living forms and their constraints.

Some organic material is carried to the sea by rivers, and some is manufactured in shallow water by attached plants. More than 90 percent of the basic organic material that fuels and builds the life in the sea, however, is synthesized within the lighted surface layers of open water by the many varieties of phytoplankton. These sunny pastures of plant cells are grazed by the herbivorous zooplankton (small planktonic animals) and by some small fishes. These in turn are prey to various carnivorous creatures, large and small, who have their predators also.

The debris from the activities in the surface layers settles into the dimly lighted and unlighted midlayers of the sea, the twilight mesopelagic zone and the midnight bathypelagic zone, to serve as one source of food for their strange inhabitants. This process depletes the surface layers of some food and particularly of the vital plant nutrients, or fertilizers, that become trapped below the surface layers, where they are unavailable to the plants. Food and nutrients are also actively carried downward from the surface by vertically migrating animals.

The depleted remnants of this constant "rain" of detritus continue to the sea floor and support those animals that live just above the bottom (epibenthic animals), on the bottom (benthic animals) and burrowed into the bottom. Here filter-feeding and burrowing (deposit-feeding) animals and bacteria rework the remaining refractory particles. The more active animals also find repast in mid-water creatures and in the occasional falls of carcasses and other larger debris. Except in unusual small areas there is an abundance of oxygen in the deep water, and the solid bottom presents advantages that allow the support of a denser population of larger creatures than can exist in deep mid-water.

In shallower water such as banks, atolls, continental shelves and shallow seas conditions associated with a solid bottom and other regional modifications of the general regime enable rich populations to develop. Such areas constitute about 7 percent of the total area of the ocean. In some of these regions added food results from the growth of larger fixed plants and from land drainage.

With the above bare recitation for general orientation, I shall now discuss these matters in more detail.

The cycle of life in the sea, like that on land, is fueled by the sun's visible light acting on green plants. Of every million photons of sunlight reaching the earth's surface, some 90 enter into the net production of basic food. Perhaps 50 of the 90 contribute to the growth of

NEW EVIDENCE that an abundance of large active fishes inhabit the deep-sea floor was obtained recently by the author and his colleagues in the form of photographs such as the one on the opposite page. The photograph was made by a camera hovering over a five-gallon bait can at a depth of 1,400 meters off Lower California. The diagonal of the bait can measures a foot. The larger fish are mostly rat-tailed grenadiers and sablefish. The fact that large numbers of such fish are attracted almost immediately to the bait suggests that two rather independent branches of the marine food web coexist in support of the deep-bottom creatures by dead material: the rain of fine detritus, which supports a variety of attached filter-feeding and burrowing organisms, and rare, widely separated falls of large food fragments, which support active creatures adapted to the discovery and utilization of such food.

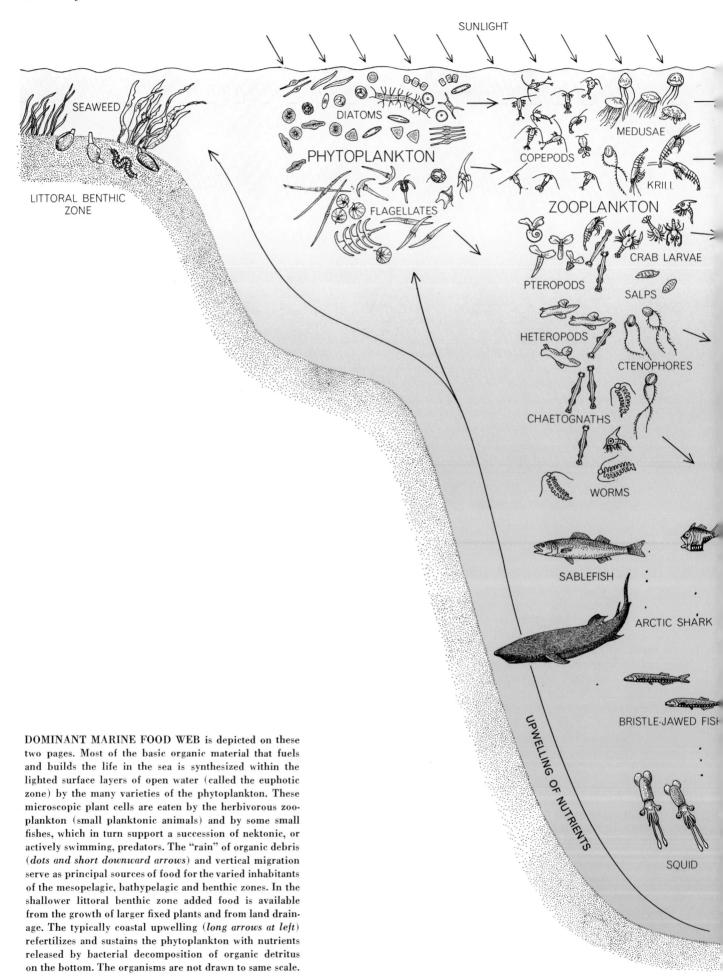

SUNLIGHT

SEAWEED

LITTORAL BENTHIC
ZONE

DIATOMS

PHYTOPLANKTON

FLAGELLATES

MEDUSAE

COPEPODS

KRILL

ZOOPLANKTON

CRAB LARVAE

PTEROPODS

SALPS

HETEROPODS

CTENOPHORES

CHAETOGNATHS

WORMS

SABLEFISH

ARCTIC SHARK

BRISTLE-JAWED FISH

UPWELLING OF NUTRIENTS

SQUID

DOMINANT MARINE FOOD WEB is depicted on these two pages. Most of the basic organic material that fuels and builds the life in the sea is synthesized within the lighted surface layers of open water (called the euphotic zone) by the many varieties of the phytoplankton. These microscopic plant cells are eaten by the herbivorous zooplankton (small planktonic animals) and by some small fishes, which in turn support a succession of nektonic, or actively swimming, predators. The "rain" of organic debris (*dots and short downward arrows*) and vertical migration serve as principal sources of food for the varied inhabitants of the mesopelagic, bathypelagic and benthic zones. In the shallower littoral benthic zone added food is available from the growth of larger fixed plants and from land drainage. The typically coastal upwelling (*long arrows at left*) refertilizes and sustains the phytoplankton with nutrients released by bacterial decomposition of organic detritus on the bottom. The organisms are not drawn to same scale.

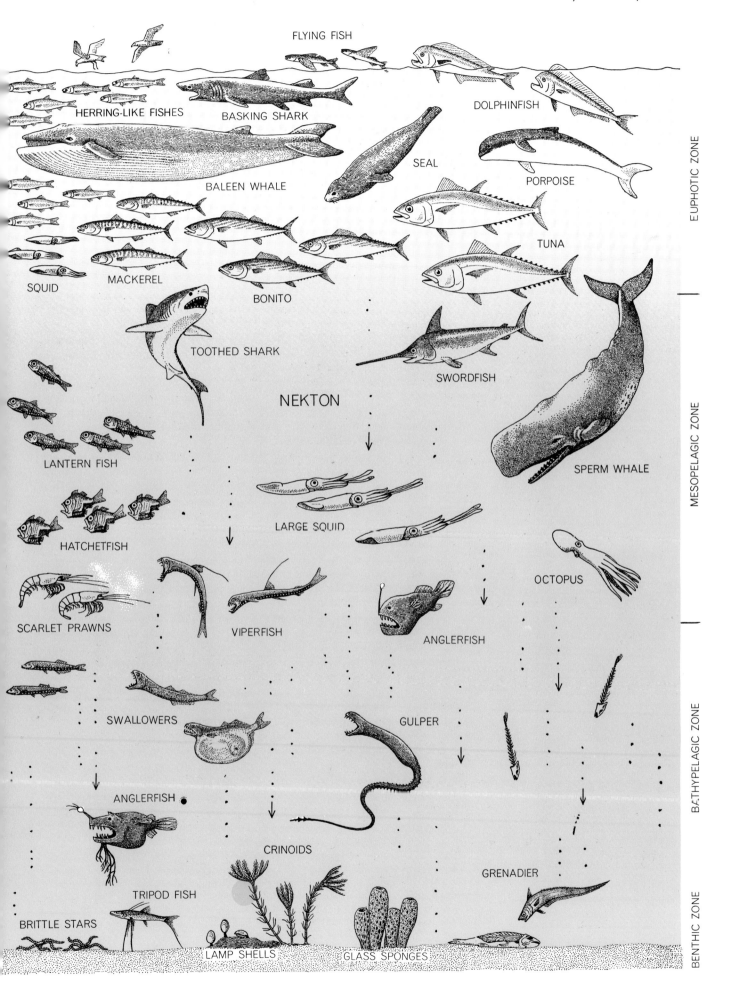

FLYING FISH

HERRING-LIKE FISHES   BASKING SHARK   DOLPHINFISH

SEAL   PORPOISE

BALEEN WHALE

TUNA

SQUID   MACKEREL   BONITO

TOOTHED SHARK   SWORDFISH

NEKTON   SPERM WHALE

LANTERN FISH

HATCHETFISH   LARGE SQUID   OCTOPUS

SCARLET PRAWNS   VIPERFISH   ANGLERFISH

SWALLOWERS   GULPER

ANGLERFISH   CRINOIDS   GRENADIER

TRIPOD FISH

BRITTLE STARS   LAMP SHELLS   GLASS SPONGES

EUPHOTIC ZONE

MESOPELAGIC ZONE

BATHYPELAGIC ZONE

BENTHIC ZONE

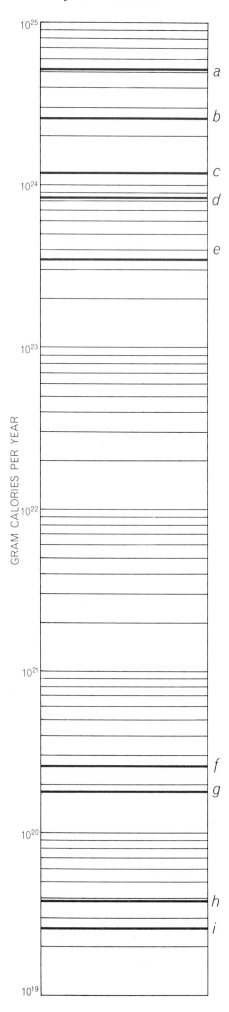

land plants and about 40 to the growth of the single-celled green plants of the sea, the phytoplankton [*see illustration at left*]. It is this minute fraction of the sun's radiant energy that supplies the living organisms of this planet not only with their food but also with a breathable atmosphere.

The terrestrial and marine plants and animals arose from the same sources, through similar evolutionary sequences and by the action of the same natural laws. Yet these two living systems differ greatly at the stage in which we now view them. Were we to imagine a terrestrial food web that had developed in a form limited to that of the open sea, we would envision the land populated predominantly by short-lived simple plant cells grazed by small insects, worms and snails, which in turn would support a sparse predaceous population of larger insects, birds, frogs and lizards. The population of still larger carnivores would be a small fraction of the populations of large creatures that the existing land food web can nurture, because organisms in each of these steps pass on not more than 15 percent of the organic substance.

In some important respects this imaginary condition is not unlike that of the dominant food web of the sea, where almost all marine life is sustained by microscopic plants and near-microscopic herbivores and carnivores, which pass on only a greatly diminished supply of food to sustain the larger, more active and more complex creatures. In other respects the analogy is substantially inaccurate, because the primary marine food production is carried out by cells dispersed widely in a dense fluid medium.

This fact of an initial dispersal imposes a set of profound general conditions on all forms of life in the sea. For comparison, the concentration of plant food in a moderately rich grassland is of the order of a thousandth of the volume of the gross space it occupies and of the order of half of the mass of the air in which it is immersed. In moderately rich areas of the sea, on the other hand, food

is hundreds of times more dilute in volume and hundreds of thousands of times more dilute in relative mass. To crop this meager broth a blind herbivore or a simple pore in a filtering structure would need to process a weight of water hundreds of thousands of times the weight of the cell it eventually captures. In even the densest concentrations the factor exceeds several thousands, and with each further step in the food web dilution increases. Thus from the beginnings of the marine food web we see many adaptations accommodating to this dilution: eyes in microscopic herbivorous animals, filters of exquisite design, mechanisms and behavior for discovering local concentrations, complex search gear and, on the bottom, attachments to elicit the aid of moving water in carrying out the task of filtration. All these adaptations stem from the conditions that limit plant life in the open sea to microscopic dimensions.

It is in the sunlit near-surface of the open sea that the unique nature of the dominant system of marine life is irrevocably molded. The near-surface, or mixed, layer of the sea varies in thickness from tens of feet to hundreds depending on the nature of the general circulation, mixing by winds and heating [see "The Atmosphere and the Ocean," by R. W. Stewart, page 27]. Here the basic food production of the sea is accomplished by single-celled plants. One common group of small phytoplankton are the coccolithophores, with calcareous plates, a swimming ability and often an oil droplet for food storage and buoyancy. The larger microscopic phytoplankton are composed of many species belonging to several groups: naked algal cells, diatoms with complex shells of silica and actively swimming and rotating flagellates. Very small forms of many groups are also abundant and collectively are called nannoplankton.

The species composition of the phytoplankton is everywhere complex and varies from place to place, season to season and year to year. The various regions of the ocean are typified, however, by

PRODUCTIVITY of the land and the sea are compared in terms of the net amount of energy that is converted from sunlight to organic matter by the green cells of land and sea plants. Colored lines denote total energy reaching the earth's upper atmosphere (*a*), total energy reaching earth's surface (*b*), total energy usable for photosynthesis (*c*), total energy usable for photosynthesis at sea (*d*), total energy usable for photosynthesis on land (*e*), net energy used for photosynthesis on land (*f*), net energy used for photosynthesis at sea (*g*), net energy used by land herbivores (*h*) and net energy used by sea herbivores (*i*). Although more sunlight falls on the sea than on the land (by virtue of the sea's larger surface area), the total land area is estimated to outproduce the total sea area by 25 to 50 percent. This is primarily due to low nutrient concentrations in the euphotic zone and high metabolism in marine plants. The data are from Walter R. Schmitt of Scripps Institution of Oceanography.

dominant major groups and particular species. Seasonal effects are often strong, with dense blooms of phytoplankton occurring when high levels of plant nutrients suddenly become usable or available, such as in high latitudes in spring or along coasts at the onset of upwelling. The concentration of phytoplankton varies on all dimensional scales, even down to small patches.

It is not immediately obvious why the dominant primary production of organic matter in the sea is carried out by microscopic single-celled plants instead of free-floating higher plants or other intermediate plant forms. The question arises: Why are there no pelagic "trees" in the ocean? One can easily compute the advantages such a tree would enjoy, with its canopy near the surface in the lighted levels and its trunk and roots extending down to the nutrient-rich waters under the mixed layer. The answer to this fundamental question probably has several parts. The evolution of plants in the pelagic realm favored smallness rather than expansion because the mixed layer in which these plants live is quite homogeneous; hence small incremental extensions from a plant cell cannot aid it in bridging to richer sources in order to satisfy its several needs.

On land, light is immediately above the soil and nutrients are immediately below; thus any extension is of immediate benefit, and the development of single cells into higher erect plants is able to follow in a stepwise evolutionary sequence. At sea the same richer sources exist but are so far apart that only a very large ready-made plant could act as a bridge between them. Although such plants could develop in some other environment and then adapt to the pelagic conditions, this has not come about. It is difficult to see how such a plant would propagate anyway; certainly it could not propagate in the open sea, because the young plants there would be at a severe disadvantage. In the sea small-scale differential motions of water are rapidly damped out, and any free-floating plant must often depend on molecular diffusion in the water for the uptake of nutrients and excretion of wastes. Smallness and self-motion are then advantageous, and a gross structure of cells cannot exchange nutrients or wastes as well as the same cells can separately or in open aggregations.

In addition the large-scale circulation of the ocean continuously sweeps the pelagic plants out of the region to which they are best adapted. It is essential that some individuals be returned to renew

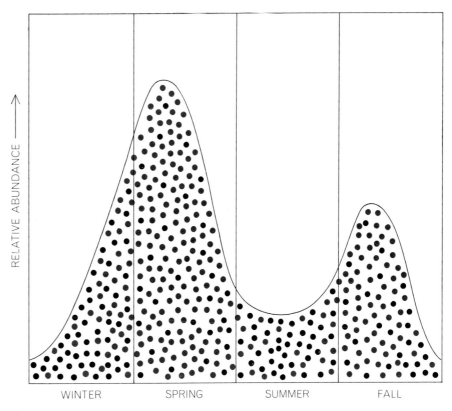

SPECIES COMPOSITION AND ABUNDANCE of the phytoplankton varies from season to season, particularly at high latitudes. During the winter the turbulence caused by storms replenishes the supply of nutrients in the surface layers. During this period flagellates (*black dots*) tend to dominate. In early spring the increase in the amount of sunlight reaching the surface stimulates plant growth, and diatoms (*colored dots*) are stimulated to grow. Later in spring grazing by zooplankton and a decrease in the supply of nutrients caused by calmer weather result in a general reduction in the phytoplankton population, which reaches a secondary minimum in midsummer, during which time flagellates again dominate. The increased mixing caused by early autumn storms causes a rise in the supply of nutrients and a corresponding minor surge in the population of diatoms. The decreasing sunlight of late fall and grazing by zooplankton again reduce the general level of the plant population.

the populations. More mechanisms for this essential return exist for single-celled plants than exist for large plants, or even for any conventional spores, seeds or juveniles. Any of these can be carried by oceanic gyres or diffused by large-scale motions of surface eddies and periodic counterflow, but single-celled plants can also ride submerged countercurrents while temporarily feeding on food particles or perhaps on dissolved organic material. Other mechanisms of distribution undoubtedly are also occasionally important. For example, living marine plant cells are carried by storm-borne spray, in bird feathers and by well-fed fish and birds in their undigested food.

No large plant has solved the many problems of development, dispersal and reproduction. There *are* no pelagic trees, and these several factors in concert therefore restrict the open sea in a profound way. They confine it to an initial food web composed of microscopic forms, whereas larger plants live attached only to shallow bottoms (which

comprise some 2 percent of the ocean area). Attached plants, unlike free-floating plants, are not subject to the aforementioned limitations. For attached plants all degrees of water motion enhance the exchange of nutrients and wastes. Moreover, their normal population does not drift, much of their reproduction is by budding, and their spores are adapted for rapid development and settlement. Larger plants too are sometimes found in nonreproducing terminal accumulations of drifting shore plants in a few special convergent deep-sea areas such as the Sargasso Sea.

Although species of phytoplankton will populate only regions with conditions to which they are adapted, factors other than temperature, nutrients and light levels undoubtedly are important in determining the species composition of phytoplankton populations. Little is understood of the mechanisms that give rise to an abundance of particular species under certain conditions. Grazing herbivores may consume only a part of the size range of cells, allowing certain sizes and types to dominate temporarily. Little is understood of the mechanisms that give rise to an abundance of particular species under certain conditions. Chemical by-products of certain species probably exclude certain other species. Often details of individual cell behavior are probably also important in the introduction and success of a species in a particular area. In some cases we can glimpse what these mechanisms are.

For example, both the larger diatoms and the larger flagellates can move at appreciable velocities through the water. The diatoms commonly sink downward, whereas the flagellates actively swim upward toward light. These are probably patterns of behavior primarily for increasing exchange, but the interaction of such unidirectional motions with random turbulence or systematic convective motion is not simple, as it is with an inactive particle. Rather, we would expect diatoms to be statistically abundant in upward-moving water and to sink out of the near-surface layers when turbulence or upward convection is low.

Conversely, flagellates should be statistically more abundant in downwelling water and should concentrate near the surface in low turbulence and slow downward water motions. These effects seem to exist. Off some continental coasts in summer flagellates may eventually collect in high concentrations. As they begin to shade one another from the light, each individual struggles closer to the lighted surface, producing such a high density that large areas of the water are turned red or brown by their pigments. The concentration of flagellates in these "red tides" sometimes becomes too great for their own survival. Several species of flagellates also become highly toxic as they grow older. Thus they sometimes both produce and participate in a mass death of fish and invertebrates that has been known to give rise to such a high yield of hydrogen sulfide as to blacken the white houses of coastal cities.

Large diatom cells, on the other hand, spend a disproportionately greater time in upward-moving regions of the water and an unlimited time in any region where the upward motion about equals their own downward motion. (The support of unidirectionally moving objects by contrary environmental motion is observed in other phenomena, such as the production of rain and hail.) Diatom cells are thus statistically abundant in upwelling water, and the distribution of diatoms probably is often a reflection of the turbulent-convective regime of the water. Sinking and the dependence of

the larger diatoms on upward convection and turbulence for support aids them in reaching upwelling regions, where nutrients are high; it helps to explain their dominance in such regions and such other features of their distribution as their high proportion in rich ocean regions and their frequent inverse occurrence with flagellates. Differences in adaptations to the physical and chemical conditions, and the release of chemical products, probably reinforce such relations.

In some areas, such as parts of the equatorial current system and shallow seas, where lateral and vertical circulation is rapid, the species composition of phytoplankton is perhaps more simply

a result of the inherent ability of the species to grow, survive and reproduce under the local conditions of temperature, light, nutrients, competitors and herbivores. Elsewhere second-order effects of the detailed cell behavior often dominate. Those details of behavior that give rise to concentrations on any dimensional scale are particularly important to all subsequent steps in the food chain.

All phytoplankton cells eventually settle from the surface layers. The depletion of nutrients and food from the surface layers takes place continuously through the loss of organic material, plant cells, molts, bodies of animals, fecal pellets and so forth, which release their content of chemical nutrients at

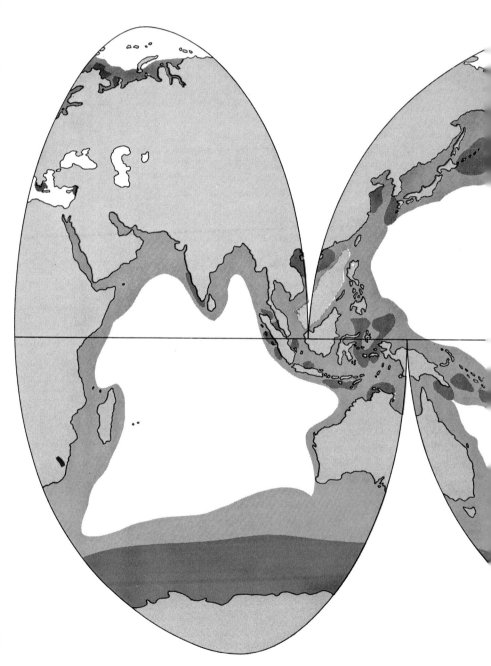

FAVORABLE CONDITIONS for the growth of phytoplankton occur wherever upwelling or mixing tends to bring subsurface nutrients up to the euphotic layer of the ocean. This map,

various depths through the action of bacteria and other organisms. The periodic downward migration of zooplankton further contributes to this loss.

These nutrients are "trapped" below the level of light adequate to sustain photosynthesis, and therefore the water in which plants must grow generally contains very low concentrations of such vital substances. It is this condition that is principally responsible for the comparatively low total net productivity of the sea compared with that of the land. The regions where trapping is broken down or does not exist—where there is upwelling of nutrient-rich water along coasts, in parts of the equatorial regions, in the wakes of islands and banks and in high latitudes, and where there is rapid recirculation of nutrients over shallow shelves and seas—locally bear the sea's richest fund of life.

The initial factors discussed so far have placed an inescapable stamp on the form of all life in the open sea, as irrevocably no doubt as the properties and distribution of hydrogen have dictated the form of the universe. These factors have limited the dominant form of life in the sea to an initial microscopic sequence that is relatively unproductive, is stimulated by upwelling and mixing and is otherwise altered in species composition and distribution by physical, chemical and biological processes on all dimensional scales. The same factors also limit the populations of higher animals and have led to unexpectedly simple adaptations, such as the sinking of the larger diatoms as a tactic to solve the manifold problems of enhancing nutrient and waste exchange, finding nutrients, remaining in the surface waters and repopulating.

The grazing of the phytoplankton is principally conducted by the herbivorous members of the zooplankton, a heterogeneous group of small animals that carry out several steps in the food web as herbivores, carnivores and detrital (debris-eating) feeders. Among the important members of the zooplankton are the arthropods, animals with external

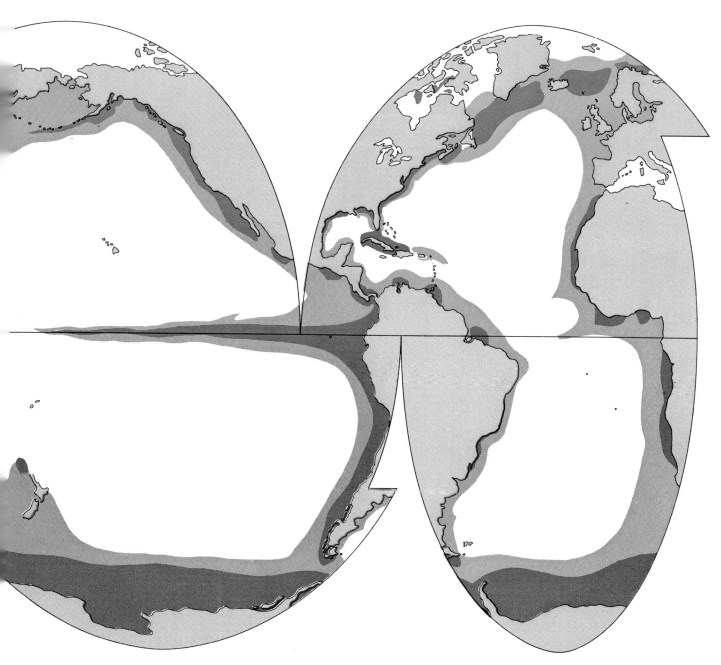

which is adapted from one compiled by the Norwegian oceanographer Harald U. Sverdrup, shows the global distribution of such waters, in which the productivity of marine life would be expected to be very high (*dark color*) and moderately high (*light color*).

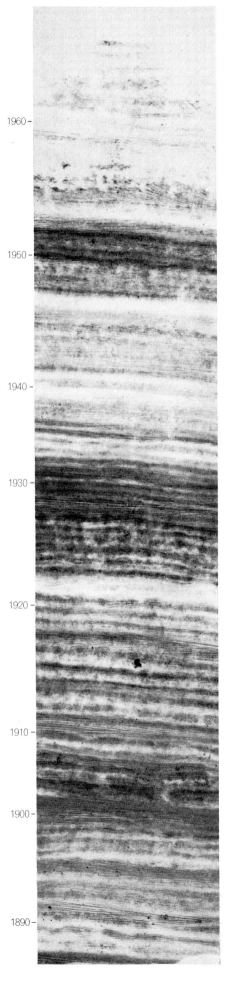

1960 –

1950 –

1940 –

1930 –

1920 –

1910 –

1900 –

1890 –

skeletons that belong to the same broad group as insects, crabs and shrimps. The planktonic arthropods include the abundant copepods, which are in a sense the marine equivalent of insects. Copepods are represented in the sea by some 10,-000 or more species that act not only as herbivores, carnivores or detrital feeders but also as external or even internal parasites! Two or three thousand of these species live in the open sea. Other important arthropods are the shrimplike euphausiids, the strongest vertical migrators of the zooplankton. They compose the vast shoals of krill that occur in high latitudes and that constitute one of the principal foods of the baleen whales. The zooplankton also include the strange bristle-jawed chaetognaths, or arrowworms, carnivores of mysterious origin and affinities known only in the marine environment. Widely distributed and abundant, the chaetognaths are represented by a surprisingly small number of species, perhaps fewer than 50. Larvae of many types, worms, medusae (jellyfish), ctenophores (comb jellies), gastropods (snails), pteropods and heteropods (other pelagic mollusks), salps, unpigmented flagellates and many others are also important components of this milieu, each with its own remarkably complex and often bizarre life history, behavior and form.

The larger zooplankton are mainly carnivores, and those of herbivorous habit are restricted to feeding on the larger plant cells. Much of the food supply, however, exists in the form of very small particles such as the nannoplankton, and these appear to be available almost solely to microscopic creatures. The immense distances between plant cells, many thousands of times their diameter, place a great premium on the development of feeding mechanisms that avoid the simple filtering of water

RARE SEDIMENTARY RECORD of the recent annual oceanographic, meteorological and biological history of part of a major oceanic system is revealed in this radiograph of a section of an ocean-bottom core obtained by Andrew Soutar of the Scripps Institution of Oceanography in the Santa Barbara Basin off the California coast. In some near-shore basins such as this one the absence of oxygen causes refractory parts of the organic debris to be left undecomposed and the sediment to remain undisturbed in the annual layers called varves. The dark layers are the densest and represent winter sedimentation. The lighter and less dense layers are composed mostly of diatoms and represent spring and summer sedimentation.

through fine pores. The power necessary to maintain a certain rate of flow through pores or nets increases inversely at an exponential rate with respect to the pore or mesh diameter, and the small planktonic herbivores, detrital feeders and carnivores show many adaptations to avoid this energy loss. Eyesight has developed in many minute animals to make possible selective capture. A variety of webs, bristles, rakes, combs, cilia and other structures are found, and they are often sticky. Stickiness allows the capture of food that is finer than the interspaces in the filtering structures, and it greatly reduces the expenditure of energy.

A few groups have developed extremely fine and apparently quite effective nets. One group that has accomplished this is the Larvacea. A larvacian produces and inhabits a complex external "house," much larger than its owner, that contains a system of very finely constructed nets through which the creature maintains a gentle flow [*see illustration on page 76*]. The Larvacea have apparently solved the problem of energy loss in filtering by having proportionately large nets, fine strong threads and a low rate of flow.

The composition of the zooplankton differs from place to place, day to night, season to season and year to year, yet most species are limited in distribution, and the members of the planktonic communities commonly show a rather stable representation of the modes of life.

The zooplankton are, of course, faced with the necessity of maintaining breeding assemblages and, like the phytoplankton, with the necessity of establishing a reinoculation of parent waters. In addition, their behavior must lead to a correspondence with their food and to the pattern of large-scale and small-scale spottiness already imposed on the marine realm by the phytoplankton. The swimming powers of the larger zooplankton are quite adequate for finding local small-scale patches of food. That this task is accomplished on a large scale is indirectly demonstrated by the observed correspondence between the quantities of zooplankton and the plant nutrients in the surface waters. How this large-scale task is accomplished is understood for some groups. For example, some zooplankton species have been shown to descend near the end of suitable conditions at the surface and to take temporary residence in a submerged countercurrent that returns them upstream.

There are many large and small puz-

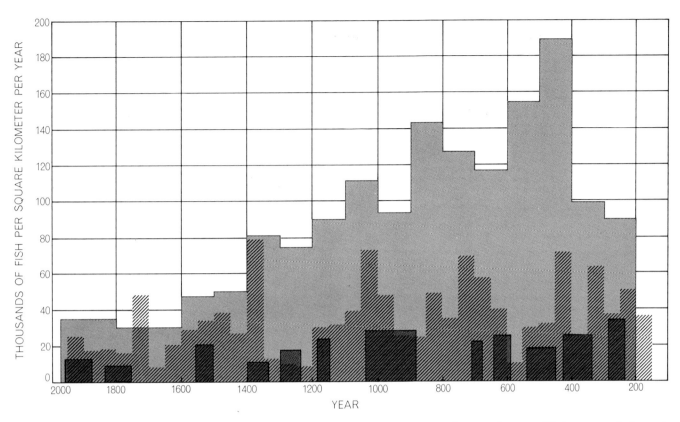

ESTIMATED FISH POPULATIONS in the Santa Barbara Basin over the past 1,800 years were obtained for three species by counting the average number of scales of each species in the varves of the core shown on the opposite page. Minimum population estimates for fish one year old and older are given for Pacific sardines (*gray*), northern sardines (*colored areas*) and Pacific hake (*hatched*).

zles in the distribution of zooplankton. As an example, dense concentrations of phytoplankton are often associated with low populations of zooplankton. These are probably rapidly growing blooms that zooplankton have not yet invaded and grazed on, but it is not completely clear that this is so. Chemical repulsion may be involved.

The concentration of larger zooplankton and small fish in the surface layers is much greater at night than during the day, because of a group of strongly swimming members that share their time between the surface and the mesopelagic region. This behavior is probably primarily a tactic to enjoy the best of two worlds: to crop the richer food developing in the surface layers and to minimize mortality from predation by remaining always in the dark, like timid rabbits emerging from the thicket to graze the nighttime fields, although still in the presence of foxes and ferrets. Many small zooplankton organisms also make a daily migration of some vertical extent.

In addition to its primary purpose daily vertical migration undoubtedly serves the migrating organisms in a number of other ways. It enables the creatures to adjust their mean temperature, so that by spending the days in cooler water the amount of food used during rest is reduced. Perhaps such processes as the rate of egg development are also controlled by these tactics. Many land animals employ hiding behavior for similar kinds of adjustment. Convincing arguments have also been presented to show that vertical migration serves to maintain a wide range of tolerance in the migrating species, so that they will be more successful under many more conditions than if they lived solely in the surface layers. This migration must also play an important part in the distribution of many species. Interaction of the daily migrants with the water motion produced by daily land-sea breeze alternation can hold the migrants offshore by a kind of "rectification" of the oscillating water motion. More generally, descent into the lower layers increases the influence of submerged countercurrents, thereby enhancing the opportunity to return upstream, to enter upwelling regions and hence to find high nutrient levels and associated high phytoplankton productivity.

Even minor details of behavior may strongly contribute to success. Migrants spend the day at a depth corresponding to relatively constant low light levels, where the movement of the water commonly is different from that at the surface. Most of the members rise somewhat even at the passage of a cloud shadow. Should they be carried under the shadow of an area rich in phytoplankton, they migrate to shallower depths, thereby often decreasing or even halting their drift with respect to this rich region to which they will ascend at night. Conversely, when the surface waters are clear and lean, they will migrate deeper and most often drift relatively faster.

We might simplistically view the distribution of zooplankton, and phytoplankton for that matter, as the consequence of a broad inoculation of the oceans with a spectrum of species, each with a certain adaptive range of tolerances and a certain variable range of feeding, reproducing and migrating behavior. At some places and at some times the behavior of a species, interacting even in detailed secondary ways with the variable conditions of the ocean and its other inhabitants, results in temporary, seasonal or persistent success.

There are a few exceptions to the microscopic dimensions of the herbivores in the pelagic food web. Among these the herrings and herring-like fishes are able to consume phytoplankton as a substantial component of their diet. Such an adaptation gives these fishes access to many times the food supply of the more

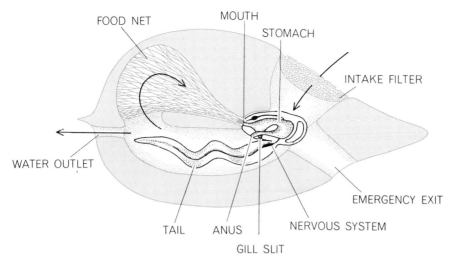

FOOD NET   MOUTH   STOMACH   INTAKE FILTER   WATER OUTLET   EMERGENCY EXIT   TAIL   ANUS   NERVOUS SYSTEM   GILL SLIT

LARVACIAN is representative of a group of small planktonic herbivores that has solved the problem of energy loss in filtering, apparently without utilizing "stickiness," by having proportionately large nets, strong fine threads and a low rate of water flow. The larvacian (*black*) produces and inhabits a complex external "house" (*color*), much larger than its owner, which contains a system of nets through which the organism maintains a gentle flow. In almost all other groups simple filters are employed only to exclude large particles.

carnivorous groups. It is therefore no surprise that the partly herbivorous fishes comprise the bulk of the world's fisheries [see "The Food Resources of the Ocean," by S. J. Holt, page 93].

The principal food supplies of the pelagic populations are passed on in incremental steps and rapidly depleted quantity to the larger carnivorous zooplankton, then to small fishes and squids, and ultimately to the wide range of larger carnivores of the pelagic realm. In this region without refuge, either powerful static defenses, such as the stinging cells of the medusae and men-o'-war, or increasing size, acuity, alertness, speed and strength are the requirements for survival at each step. Streamlining of form here reaches a high point of development, and in tropical waters it is conspicuous even in small fishes, since the lower viscosity of the warmer waters will enable a highly streamlined small prey to escape a poorly streamlined predator, an effect that exists only for fishes of twice the length in cold, viscous, arctic or deep waters.

The pelagic region contains some of the largest and most superbly designed creatures ever to inhabit this earth: the exquisitely constructed pelagic tunas; the multicolored dolphinfishes, capturers of flying fishes; the conversational porpoises; the shallow- and deep-feeding swordfishes and toothed whales, and the greatest carnivores of all, the baleen whales and some plankton-eating sharks, whose prey are entire schools of krill or small fishes. Seals and sea lions feed far into the pelagic realm. In concert with these great predators, large carnivorous

sharks await injured prey. Marine birds, some adapted to almost continuous pelagic life, consume surprising quantities of ocean food, diving, plunging, skimming and gulping in pursuit. Creatures of this region have developed such faculties as advanced sonar, unexplained senses of orientation and homing, and extreme olfactory sensitivity.

These larger creatures of the sea commonly move in schools, shoals and herds. In addition to meeting the needs of mating such grouping is advantageous in both defensive and predatory strategy, much like the cargo-ship convoy and submarine "wolf pack" of World War II. Both defensive and predatory assemblages are often complex. Small fishes of several species commonly school together. Diverse predators also form loosely cooperative groups, and many species of marine birds depend almost wholly on prey driven to the surface by submerged predators.

At night, schools of prey and predators are almost always spectacularly illuminated by bioluminescence produced by the microscopic and larger plankton. The reason for the ubiquitous production of light by the microorganisms of the sea remains obscure, and suggested explanations are controversial. It has been suggested that light is a kind of inadvertent by-product of life in transparent organisms. It has also been hypothesized that the emission of light on disturbance is advantageous to the plankton in making the predators of the plankton conspicuous to *their* predators! Unquestionably it does act this way. Indeed, some fisheries base the detection of their prey on the bioluminescence that the fish excite.

It is difficult, however, to defend the thesis that this effect was the direct factor in the original development of bioluminescence, since the effect was of no advantage to the individual microorganism that first developed it. Perhaps the luminescence of a microorganism also discourages attack by the light-avoiding zooplankton and is of initial survival benefit to the individual. As it then became general in the population, the effect of revealing plankton predators to their predators would also become important.

The fallout of organic material into the deep, dimly lighted mid-water supports a sparse population of fishes and invertebrates. Within the mesopelagic and bathypelagic zones are found some of the most curious and bizarre creatures of this earth. These range from the highly developed and powerfully predaceous intruders, toothed whales and swordfishes, at the climax of the food chain, to the remarkable squids, octopuses, euphausiids, lantern fishes, gulpers and anglerfishes that inhabit the bathypelagic region.

In the mesopelagic region, where some sunlight penetrates, fishes are often countershaded, that is, they are darker above and lighter below, as are surface fishes. Many of the creatures of this dimly lighted region participate in the daily migration, swimming to the upper layers at evening like bats emerging from their caves. At greater depths, over a half-mile or so, the common inhabitants are often darkly pigmented, weak-bodied and frequently adapted to unusual feeding techniques. Attraction of prey by luminescent lures or by mimicry of small prey, greatly extensible jaws and expansible abdomens are common. It is, however, a region of Lilliputian monsters, usually not more than six inches in length, with most larger fishes greatly reduced in musculature and weakly constructed.

There are some much larger, stronger and more active fishes and squids in this region, although they are not taken in trawls or seen from submersibles. Knowledge of their existence comes mainly from specimens found in the stomach of sperm whales and swordfish. They must be rare, however, since the slow, conservative creatures that are taken in trawls could hardly coexist with large numbers of active predators. Nevertheless, populations must be sufficiently large to attract the sperm whales and swordfish. There is evidence that the sperm whales possess highly developed long-range hunting sonar. They may locate their prey over relatively great distances, perhaps miles, from just such an extremely sparse population of active bathypelagic animals.

Although many near-surface organisms are luminescent, it is in the bathypelagic region that bioluminescence has reached a surprising level of development, with at least two-thirds of the species producing light. Were we truly marine-oriented, we would perhaps be more surprised by the almost complete absence of biological light in the land environment, with its few rare cases of fireflies, glowworms and luminous bacteria. Clearly bioluminescence can be valuable to higher organisms, and the creatures of the bathypelagic realm have developed light-producing organs and structures to a high degree. In many cases the organs have obvious functions. Some fishes, squids and euphausiids possess searchlights with reflector, lens and iris almost as complex as the eye. Others have complex patterns of small lights that may serve the functions of recognition, schooling control and even mimicry of a small group of luminous plank-

ton. Strong flashes may confuse predators by "target alteration" effects, or by producing residual images in the predators' vision. Some squids and shrimps are more direct and discharge luminous clouds to cover their escape. The luminous organs are arranged on some fishes so that they can be used to countershade their silhouettes against faint light coming from the surface. Luminous baits are well developed. Lights may also be used for locating a mate, a problem of this vast, sparsely populated domain that has been solved by some anglerfishes by the development of tiny males that live parasitically attached to their relatively huge mates.

It has been shown that the vertebrate eye has been adapted to detect objects in the lowest light level on the earth's surface—a moonless, overcast night under a dense forest canopy—but not lower. Light levels in the bathypelagic region can be much lower. This is most probably the primary difference that accounts for the absence of bioluminescence in higher land animals and the richness of its development in the ocean forms.

The densest populations of bathypelagic creatures lie below the most productive surface regions, except at high latitudes, where the dearth of winter food probably would exhaust the meager reserves of these creatures. All the bathypelagic populations are sparse, and in this region living creatures are less than one hundred-millionth of the water volume. Nevertheless, the zone is of immense dimensions and the total populations may be large. Some genera, such as the feeble, tiny bristle-jawed fishes, are probably the most numerous fishes in the world and constitute a gigantic total biomass. There are some 2,000 species of fishes and as many species of the larger invertebrates known to inhabit the bathypelagic zone, but only a few of these species appear to be widespread. The barriers to distribution in this widely interconnected mid-water region are not obvious.

The floor of the deep sea constitutes an environment quite unlike the midwater and surface environments. Here are sites for the attachment of the larger

CHAMPION FILTER FEEDER of the world ocean in terms of volume is the blue whale, a mature specimen of which lies freshly butchered on the deck of a whaling vessel in this photograph. The whale's stomach has been cut open with a flensing knife to reveal its last meal: an immense quantity of euphausiids, or krill, each measuring about three inches in length. The baleen whales are not plankton-filterers in the ordinary sense but rather are great carnivores that seek out and engulf entire schools of small fish or invertebrates. The photograph was made by Robert Clarke of the National Institute of Oceanography in Wormley, England.

invertebrates that filter detritus from the water. Among these animals are representatives of some of the earliest multicelled creatures to exist on the earth, glass sponges, sea lilies (crinoids)—once thought to have been long extinct—and lamp shells (brachiopods).

At one time it was also thought that the abyssal floor was sparsely inhabited and that the populations of the deep-ocean floor were supplied with food only by the slow, meager rain of terminal detrital food material that has passed through the surface and bathypelagic populations. Such refractory material requires further passage into filter feeders or through slow bacterial action in the sediment, followed by consumption by larger burrowing organisms, before it becomes available to active free-living animals. This remnant portion of the food web could support only a very small active population.

Recent exploration of the abyssal realm with a baited camera throws doubt on the view that this is the exclusive mechanism of food transfer to the deep bottom. Large numbers of active fishes and other creatures are attracted to the bait almost immediately [see illustration on page 66]. It is probably true that several rather independent branches of the food web coexist in support of the deep-bottom creatures: one the familiar rain of fine detritus, and the other the rare, widely separated falls of large food particles that are in excess of the local feeding capacity of the broadly diffuse bathypelagic population. Such falls would include dead whales, large sharks or other large fishes and fragments of these, the multitude of remnants that are left when predators attack a school of surface fish and now, undoubtedly, garbage from ships and kills from underwater explosions. These sources result in an influx of high-grade food to the sea floor, and we would expect to find a population of active creatures adapted to its prompt discovery and utilization. The baited cameras have demonstrated that this is so.

Other sources of food materials are braided into these two extremes of the abyssal food web. There is the rather subtle downward diffusion of living and dead food that results initially from the daily vertical migration of small fish and zooplankton near the surface. This migration appears to impress a sympathetic daily migration on the mid-water populations down to great depths, far below the levels that light penetrates. Not only may such vertical migration bring feeble bathypelagic creatures near the bottom but also it accelerates in itself the flux of

dead food material to the bottom of the deep sea.

There must also be some unassignable flux of food to the abyssal population resulting from the return of juveniles to their habitat. The larvae and young of many abyssal creatures develop at much shallower levels. To the extent that the biomass of juveniles returning to the deep regions exceeds the biomass of spawn released from it, this process, which might be called "Faginism," constitutes an input of food.

Benthic animals are much more abundant in the shallower waters off continents, particularly offshore from large rivers. Here there is often not only a richer near-surface production and a less hazardous journey of food to the sea floor but also a considerable input of food conveyed by rivers to the bottom. The deep slopes of river sediment wedges are typified by a comparatively rich population of burrowing and filtering animals that utilize this fine organic material. All the great rivers of the world save one, the Congo, have built sedimentary wedges along broad reaches of their coast, and in many instances these wedges extend into deep water. The shallow regions of such wedges are highly productive of active and often valuable marine organisms. At all depths the wedges bear larger populations than are common at similar depths elsewhere. Thus one wonders what inhabits the fan of the Congo. That great river, because of a strange invasion of a submarine canyon into its month, has built no wedge but rather is depositing a vast alluvial fan in the two-mile depths of the Angola Basin. This great deep region of the sea floor may harbor an unexplored population that is wholly unique.

In itself the pressure of the water at great depths appears to constitute no insurmountable barrier to water-breathing animal life. The depth limitations of many creatures are the associated conditions of low temperature, darkness, sparse food and so on. It should perhaps come as no surprise, therefore, that some of the fishes of high latitudes, which are of course adapted to cold dark waters, extend far into the deep cold waters in much more southern latitudes. Off the coast of Lower California, in water 1,200 to 6,000 feet deep, baited cameras have found an abundance of several species of fishes that are known at the near surface only far to the north. These include giant arctic sharks, sablefish and others. It appears that some of the fishes that have been called arctic species are actually fishes of the dark cold waters of the seas,

which only "outcrop" in the Arctic, where cold water is at the surface.

I have discussed several of the benthic and epibenthic environments without pointing out some of the unique features the presence of a solid interface entails. The bottom is much more variable than the mid-water zone is. There are as a result more environmental niches for an organism to occupy, and hence we see organisms that are of a wider range of form and habit. Adaptations develop for hiding and ambuscade, for mimicry and controlled patterns. Nests and burrows can be built, lairs occupied and defended and booby traps set.

Aside from the wide range of form and function the benthic environment elicits from its inhabitants, there are more fundamental conditions that influence the nature and form of life there. For example, the dispersed food material settling from the upper layers becomes much concentrated against the sea floor. Indeed, it may become further concentrated by lateral currents moving it into depressions or the troughs of ripples.

In the mid-water environment most creatures must move by their own energies to seek food, using their own food stores for this motion. On the bottom, however, substantial water currents are present at all depths, and creatures can await the passage of their food. Although this saving only amounts to an added effectiveness for predators, it is of critical importance to those organisms that filter water for the fine food material it contains, and it is against the bottom interface that a major bypass to the microscopic steps of the dominant food web is achieved. Here large organisms can grow by consuming microscopic or even submicroscopic food particles. Clams, scallops, mussels, tube worms, barnacles and a host of other creatures that inhabit this zone have developed a wide range of extremely effective filtering mechanisms. In one step, aided by their attachment, the constant currents and the concentration of detritus against the interface, they perform the feat, most unusual in the sea, of growing large organisms directly from microscopic food.

Although the benthic environment enables the creatures of the sea to develop a major branch of the food web that is emancipated from successive microscopic steps, this makes little difference to the food economy of the sea. The sea is quite content with a large population of tiny organisms. From man's standpoint, however, the shallow benthic environment is an unusually effective producer of larger creatures for his food, and he widely utilizes these resources.

Man may not have created an ideal environment for himself, but of all the environments of the sea it is difficult to conceive of one better for its inhabitants than the one marine creatures have created almost exclusively for themselves: the coral islands and coral reefs. In these exquisite, immense and well-nigh unbelievable structures form and adaptation reach a zenith.

An adequate description of the coral reef and coral atoll structure, environments and living communities is beyond the scope of this article. The general history and structure of atolls is well known, not only because of an inherent fascination with the magic and beauty of coral islands but also because of the wide admiration and publicity given to the prescient deductions on the origin of atolls by Charles Darwin, who foresaw much of what modern exploration has affirmed.

From their slowly sinking foundations of ancient volcanic mountains, the creatures of the coral shoals have erected the greatest organic structures that exist. Even the smallest atoll far surpasses any of man's greatest building feats, and a large atoll structure in actual mass approaches the total of all man's building that now exists.

These are living monuments to the success of an extremely intricate but balanced society of fish, invertebrates and plants, capitalizing on the basic advantages of benthic populations already discussed. Here, however, each of the reef structures acts almost like a single great isolated and complex benthic organism that has extended itself from the deep poor waters to the sunlit richer surface. The trapping of the advected food from the surface currents enriches the entire community. Attached plants further add to the economy, and there is considerable direct consumption of plant life by large invertebrates and fish. Some of the creatures and relationships that have developed in this environment are among the most highly adapted found on the earth. For example, a number of the important reef-building animals, the corals, the great tridacna clams and others not only feed but also harbor within their tissues dense populations of single-celled green plants. These plants photosynthesize food that is then directly available within the bodies of the animals; the plants in turn depend on the animal waste products within the body fluids, with which they are bathed, to derive their basic nutrients. Thus within the small environment of these plant-animal composites both the entire laborious nutrient cycle and the microscopic food web of the sea appear to be substantially bypassed.

There is much unknown and much to be discovered in the structure and ecology of coral atolls. Besides the task of unraveling the complex relationships of its inhabitants there are many questions such as: Why have many potential atolls never initiated effective growth and remained submerged almost a mile below the surface? Why have others lost the race with submergence in recent times and now become shallowly submerged, dying banks? Can the nature of the circulation of the ancient ocean be deduced from the distribution of successful and unsuccessful atolls? Is there circulation within the coral limestone structure that adds to the nutrient supply, and is this related to the curious development of coral knolls, or coral heads, within the lagoons? Finally, what is the potential of cultivation within these vast, shallow-water bodies of the deep open sea?

There is, of course, much to learn about all marine life: the basic processes of the food web, productivity, populations, distributions and the mechanisms of reinoculation, and the effects of intervention into these processes, such as pollution, artificial upwelling, transplantation, cultivation and fisheries. To learn of these processes and effects we must understand the nature not only of strong simple actions but also of weak complex interactions, since the forms of life or the success of a species may be determined by extremely small second- and third-order effects. In natural affairs, unlike human codes, *de minimis curat lex—* the law *is* concerned with trivia!

Little is understood of the manner in which speciation (that is, the evolution of new species) occurs in the broadly intercommunicating pelagic environment with so few obvious barriers. Important yet unexpected environmental niches may exist in which temporary isolation may enable a new pelagic species to evolve. For example, the top few millimeters of the open sea have recently been shown to constitute a demanding environment with unique inhabitants. Further knowledge of such microcosms may well yield insight into speciation.

As it has in the past, further exploration of the abyssal realm will undoubtedly reveal undescribed creatures including members of groups thought long extinct, as well as commercially valuable populations. As we learn more of the conditions that control the distribution of species of pelagic organisms, we shall become increasingly competent to read the pages of the earth's marine-biological, oceanographic and meteorological history that are recorded in the sediments by organic remains. We shall know more of primordial history, the early production of a breathable atmosphere and petroleum production. Some of these deposits of sediment cover even the period of man's recorded history with a fine time resolution. From such great records we should eventually be able to increase greatly our understanding of the range and interrelations of weather, ocean conditions and biology for sophisticated and enlightened guidance of a broad spectrum of man's activities extending from meteorology and hydrology to oceanography and fisheries.

Learning and guidance of a more specific nature can also be of great practical importance. The diving physiology of marine mammals throws much light on the same physiological processes in land animals in oxygen stress (during birth, for example). The higher flowering plants that inhabit the marine salt marshes are able to tolerate salt at high concentration, desalinating seawater with the sun's energy. Perhaps the tiny molecule of DNA that commands this process is the most precious of marine-life resources for man's uses. Bred into existing crop plants, it may bring salt-water agriculture to reality and nullify the creeping scourge of salinization of agricultural soils.

Routine upstream reinoculation of preferred species of phytoplankton and zooplankton might stabilize some pelagic marine populations at high effectiveness. Transplanted marine plants and animals may also animate the dead saline lakes of continental interiors, as they have the Salton Sea of California.

The possible benefits of broad marine-biological understanding are endless. Man's aesthetic, adventurous, recreational and practical proclivities can be richly served. Most important, undoubtedly, is the intellectual promise: to learn how to approach and understand a complex system of strongly interacting biological, physical and chemical entities that is vastly more than the sum of its parts, and thus how better to understand complex man and his interactions with his complex planet, and to explore with intelligence and open eyes a huge portion of this earth, which continuously teaches that when understanding and insight are sought for their own sake, the rewards are more substantial and enduring than when they are sought for more limited goals.

VII

The Physical Resources of the Ocean

The Physical Resources of the Ocean

EDWARD WENK, JR.

They include not only the oil and minerals of the bottom and the minerals dissolved in seawater but also seawater itself and the shoreline carved by the action of the sea

en have caught fish in the ocean and extracted salt from its brine for thousands of years, but only within the past decade have they begun to appreciate the full potential of the resources of the sea. Three converging influences have been responsible for today's intensive exploration and development of these resources. First, scientific oceanography is generating new knowledge of what is in and under the sea. Second, new technologies make it feasible to reach and extract or harvest resources that were once inaccessible. Third, the growth of population and the industrialization of society are creating new demands for every kind of raw material.

The ocean's resources include the vast waters themselves, as a processing plant to convert solar energy into protein [see "The Food Resources of the Ocean," by S. J. Holt, page 93], a storehouse of dissolved minerals and fresh water, a receptacle for wastes, a source of tidal energy and a medium for new kinds of transportation. They also include the sea floor, sediments and rocks below the waters as sites of fossil fuel and mineral deposits; the seacoast as a unique resource that is vulnerable to rapid, irrevocable degradation by man.

Because the oceans are so wide and so deep, statistics on their gross resource potential are impressive. It is important to understand, however, that the immediate significance of these resources and

OFFSHORE OIL PLATFORM in the photograph on the opposite page is in Alaska's Cook Inlet, 60 miles southwest of Anchorage. Wells are drilled from derricks set over the massive legs, 14 feet in diameter. The plume of flame is burning natural gas, a waste product in this case. Oil and gas account for more than 90 percent of the value of minerals now being retrieved from the oceans.

their long-term relevance to society involve both exploration and development, and development depends on economic, social, legal and political considerations. One special feature of marine resources that may at first retard development may in the long run promote it: the fact that almost without exception sea-floor resources are in areas not subject to private ownership (although the resources will be largely privately developed). More than 85 percent of the ocean bottom lies beyond the present boundaries of national jurisdictions, and in the areas that are subject to national control the resources are considered common property. This circumstance may uniquely invoke a balancing of public and private interests, disciplined resource management and enhanced international cooperation.

The 350 million cubic miles of ocean water constitute the earth's largest continuous ore body. Dissolved solids amount to 35,000 parts per million, so that each cubic mile (4.7 billion tons of water) contains about 165 million tons of solids. Although most chemical elements have been detected (and probably all are present) in seawater, only common salt (sodium chloride), magnesium and bromine are now being extracted in significant amounts. The production of salt (which can be traced back to Neolithic times and resulted in the first U.S. patent) is currently valued at $175 million per year worldwide. Magnesium, the third most abundant element in the oceans, is by far the most valuable mineral extracted from seawater in this country, with annual production worth about $70 million. Although the ocean contains bromine in concentrations of only 65 parts per million, it is the source of 70 percent of the world's production of this element, which is used principal-

ly in antiknock compounds for gasoline. The economic recovery of other chemicals from seawater is questionable because of extraction costs. In a cubic mile of seawater the value of 17 critical metals (including cobalt, copper, gold, silver, uranium and zinc) is less than $1 million at current prices; a plant to handle a cubic mile of water per year would have to process 2.1 million gallons per minute every minute of the year, and operating it would cost significantly more than the value of all its products.

One of the potential resources of seawater that has been most difficult to extract economically is water itself—fresh water. As requirements for water for domestic use, agriculture and industry rise sharply, however, desalting the sea becomes increasingly attractive. More than 680 desalination plants with a capacity of more than 25,000 gallons of fresh water per day are now in operation or under construction around the globe, and the growth rate is projected at 25 percent per year over the next decade. The cost of desalting has been decreased by new technology to less than 85 cents per 1,000 gallons, but this is still generally prohibitive in the U.S., where the cost of 1,000 gallons of fresh water is about 35 cents. In water-deficient areas or where the local water supply is unfit for consumption, however, desalted water is competitive. This accounts for the presence of more than 50 plants in Kuwait, 22 on Ascension Island and the 2.6-million-gallon facility at Key West, the first U.S. city to obtain its water supply directly from the ocean. Considerably lower costs will be attained within the next decade where large-scale desalting operations are combined with nuclear-fueled power plants to take advantage of their output of waste heat.

Once upon a time man could safely utilize the waters of the sea as a recep-

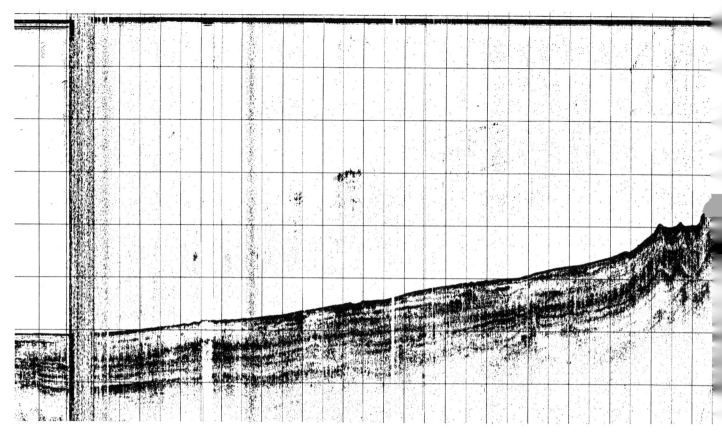

CONTINENTAL RISE, which may be rich in resources, is evident in this seismic profile made off Liberia by the Global Ocean Floor Analysis and Research Center of the U.S. Naval Oceanographic Office. The hard, straight line across the top of the record is a wa- ter reflection. The abyssal plain (*left*) is about 15,000 feet below sea level. From this plain a thick apron of land-derived layered sediments comprising the continental rise slants gently up to the toe of the continental slope. The continental slope, which is here

tacle for sewage and other effluents from municipalities and industries, confident that the wastes would rapidly be diluted, dispersed and degraded. With the growth of population and the concentration of coastal industry that is no longer possible. The sheer bulk of the material disposed of and the presence of new types of nondegradable waste products are a special threat to coastal waters— the same waters that, as we shall see, are subject to increasing demands from a wide range of competing activities. In addition pollutants are now beginning to concentrate at an alarming rate far from shore in the open ocean. Since tetraethyl lead was introduced into gasoline 45 years ago, lead concentrations in Pacific Ocean waters have jumped tenfold. Toxic DDT residues have been detected in the Bay of Bengal, having drifted with

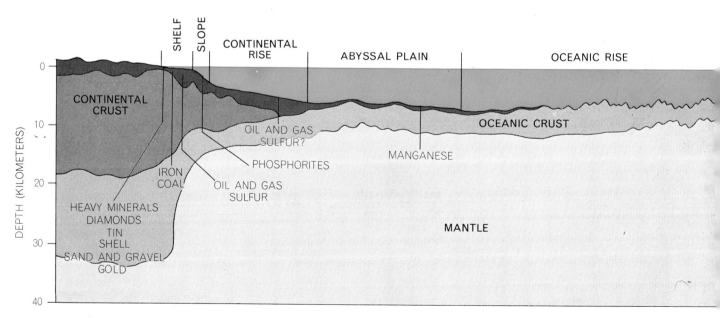

OCEAN-FLOOR RESOURCES that are known or believed to exist in the various physiographic provinces are indicated on a schemat- ic cross section of a generalized ocean basin extending from a con- tinent out to a mid-ocean ridge. Some of these resources are now

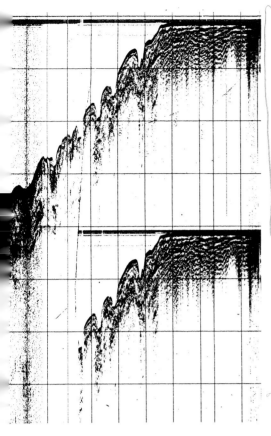

marked by large sedimentary ridges, ascends more steeply to the shallow continental shelf. The "multiple" (*right*) is in effect an echo of the structures shown above it.

the wind from as far away as Africa. And man-made radioactivity from nuclear fallout can be isolated in any 50-gallon water sample taken anywhere in the ocean.

The mineral resources of the seabed, unlike those of the essentially uniform overlying waters, occur primarily in scattered, highly localized deposits and structures on top of and within the sediments and rocks of the ocean floor. They include (1) fluids and soluble minerals, such as oil, gas, sulfur and potash, that can be extracted through boreholes; (2) consolidated subsurface deposits, such as coal, iron ore and other metals found in veins, which are so far mined only from tunnels originating on land, and (3) unconsolidated surface deposits that can be dredged, such as heavy metals in ancient beaches and stream beds, oyster shell, sand and gravel, diamonds, and "authigenic" minerals: nodules of manganese and phosphorite that have been formed by slow precipitation from seawater. Economic exploitation has so far been confined to the continental shelves in waters less than 350 feet deep and within 70 miles of the coastline.

Oil and gas represent more than 90 percent by value of all minerals obtained from the oceans and have the greatest potential for the near future. Offshore sources are responsible for 17 percent of the oil and 6 percent of the natural gas produced by non-Communist countries. Projections indicate that by 1980 a third of the oil production—four times the present output of 6.5 million barrels a day—will come from the ocean; the increase in gas production is expected to be comparable. Subsea oil and gas are now produced or are about to be produced by 28 countries; another 50 are engaged in exploratory surveys. Since 1946 more than 10,000 wells have been drilled off U.S. coasts and more than $13 billion has been invested in petroleum exploration and development. The promise of large oil reserves has stimulated industry to invest more than $1.7 billion since mid-1967 to obtain Federal leases off Louisiana, Texas and California that guarantee only the right to search for and develop unproved reserves. To date more than 6.5 million acres of the outer continental shelf off the U.S. have been leased, which is half of the acreage offered, resulting in lease income to the Federal Government of $3.4 billion. With more than 90 percent of the most favorable inland areas explored and less than 10 percent of the U.S. shelf areas surveyed in detail, the prospects are encouraging for additional large oil finds off U.S. coasts.

Sulfur, one of the world's prime industrial chemicals, is found in the cap rock of salt domes buried within continental and sea-floor sediments. The sulfur is recovered rather inexpensively by melting it with superheated water piped down from the surface and then forcing it up with compressed air. Only 5 percent of the explored salt domes contain commercial quantities of sulfur, and offshore production has been limited to two mines off Louisiana that supply two million tons, worth $37 million, a year. Now a critical shortage of sulfur and the recent discovery by the deep-drilling ship *Glomar Challenger* of sulfur-bearing domes in the deepest part of the Gulf of Mexico have stimulated an intensive search for offshore sulfur deposits.

Undersea subfloor mining can be traced back to 1620, when coal was ex-

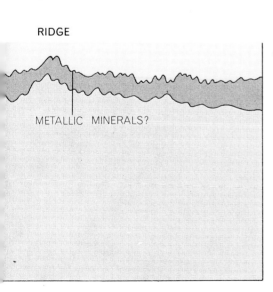

RIDGE

METALLIC MINERALS?

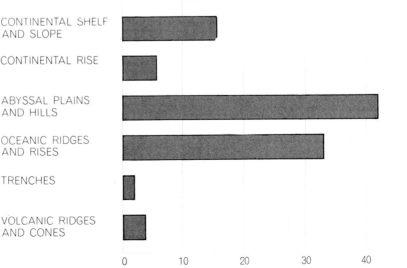

CONTINENTAL SHELF AND SLOPE					
CONTINENTAL RISE					
ABYSSAL PLAINS AND HILLS					
OCEANIC RIDGES AND RISES					
TRENCHES					
VOLCANIC RIDGES AND CONES					
0	10	20	30	40	50

being exploited but others may not be economic for years. Sedimentary layers (*black*) are the most likely site of recoverable raw materials. The chart (*right*) shows what percent of the ocean floor's 140 million square miles of area is occupied by each province.

tracted in Scotland through shafts that were driven seaward from an offshore island. To date 100 subsea mines with shaft entries on land have recovered coal, iron ore, nickel-copper ores, tin and limestone off a number of countries in all parts of the world. Coal extracted from as deep as 8,000 feet below sea level accounts for almost 30 percent of Japan's total production and more than 10 percent of Britain's. With present technology subsea mining can be conducted economically as far as 15 miles offshore, given mineral deposits that are worth $10 to $15 per ton and occur in reserves of more than $100 million. The economically feasible distance should increase to 30 miles by 1980 with the development of new methods for rapid underground excavation. Eventually shafts may be driven directly from the seabed

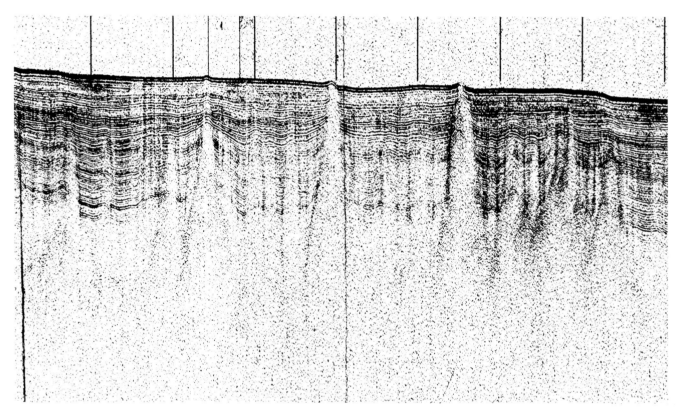

POSSIBILITY OF OIL in the deep-sea floor was revealed by this record from some 250 miles northwest of the Cape Verde Islands. The record, like the one on the preceding pages, was made by the research ship *Kane* of the Naval Oceanographic Office. The tall narrow structures appear to be salt domes, along the flanks of which surface-seeking oil is often trapped in tilted sedimentary layers.

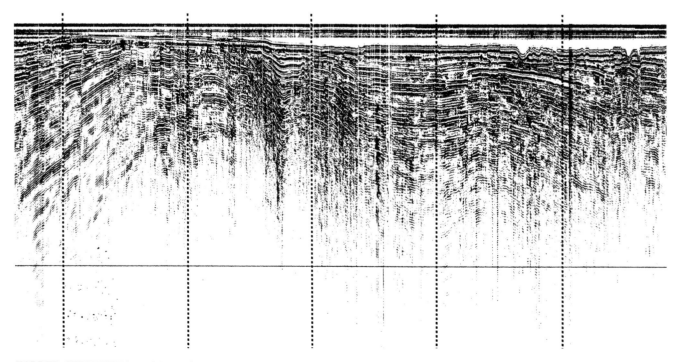

FOLDED SEDIMENTARY LAYERS are shown in this *Kane* record made on the continental shelf north of Trinidad. The band at top is from water reflections. The record shows anticlines (arches) and synclines (troughs); oil is often trapped in crests of anticlines.

if ore deposits are located in ocean-floor rock far from land.

Seventy percent of the world's continental shelves consist of ancient unconsolidated sediments from which are dredged such commodities as sand, gravel, oyster shell, tin, heavy-mineral sands and diamonds. Dredging is an attractive mining technique because of low capital investment, quick returns and high profits and the operational mobility offered by floating dredges. So far it has been limited to nearshore waters less than 235 feet deep and protected from severe weather effects. As knowledge of resources in deeper water increases, industry will undoubtedly upgrade its dredging technology.

Of the many potentially valuable surface deposits, sand and gravel are the most important in dollar terms, and only these and oyster shells are now mined off the U.S. coast. Some 20 million tons of oyster shells are extracted from U.S. continental shelves annually as a source of lime; sand and gravel run about 50 million cubic yards. As coastal metropolitan areas spread out, they cover dry-land deposits of the very construction materials required to sustain their expansion; in these circumstances sea-floor sources such as one recently found off New Jersey, which is thought to contain a billion tons of gravel, become commercially valuable.

In the deeper waters of the continental shelves, on the upper parts of the slopes and on submarine banks and ridges widespread deposits of marine phosphorite nodules are found at depths between 100 and 1,000 feet. The best-known large deposits are off southern California, where total reserves are estimated at 1.5 billion tons, and off northwestern Mexico, Peru and Chile, the southeastern U.S. and the Union of South Africa. The only major attempt at mining was made in 1961, when a company leased an area off California, but that lease was returned unexploited to the Federal Government four years later. With large land sources generally available to meet the demand for phosphates for fertilizer and other products, offshore exploitation of this resource is not likely to occur soon, except possibly in phosphate-poor countries.

The only known minerals on the floor of the deep ocean that appear to be of potential economic importance are the well-publicized manganese nodules, formed by the precipitation from seawater of manganese oxides and other mineral salts, usually on a small nucleus such as a bit of stone or a shark's tooth.

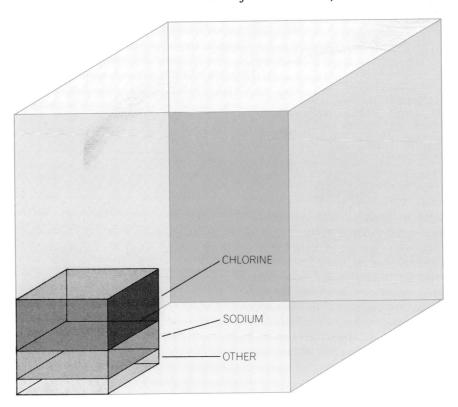

SEAWATER contains an average of 35,000 parts per million of dissolved solids. In a cubic mile of seawater, weighing 4.7 billion tons, there are therefore about 165 million tons of dissolved matter, mostly chlorine and sodium (*gray cube*). The volume of the ocean is about 350 million cubic miles, giving a theoretical mineral reserve of about 60 quadrillion tons.

ELEMENT	TONS PER CUBIC MILE	ELEMENT	TONS PER CUBIC MILE
CHLORINE	89,500,000	NICKEL	9
SODIUM	49,500,000	VANADIUM	9
MAGNESIUM	6,400,000	MANGANESE	9
SULFUR	4,200,000	TITANIUM	5
CALCIUM	1,900,000	ANTIMONY	2
POTASSIUM	1,800,000	COBALT	2
BROMINE	306,000	CESIUM	2
CARBON	132,000	CERIUM	2
STRONTIUM	38,000	YTTRIUM	1
BORON	23,000	SILVER	1
SILICON	14,000	LANTHANUM	1
FLUORINE	6,100	KRYPTON	1
ARGON	2,800	NEON	.5
NITROGEN	2,400	CADMIUM	.5
LITHIUM	800	TUNGSTEN	.5
RUBIDIUM	570	XENON	.5
PHOSPHORUS	330	GERMANIUM	.3
IODINE	280	CHROMIUM	.2
BARIUM	140	THORIUM	.2
INDIUM	94	SCANDIUM	.2
ZINC	47	LEAD	.1
IRON	47	MERCURY	.1
ALUMINUM	47	GALLIUM	.1
MOLYBDENUM	47	BISMUTH	.1
SELENIUM	19	NIOBIUM	.05
TIN	14	THALLIUM	.05
COPPER	14	HELIUM	.03
ARSENIC	14	GOLD	.02
URANIUM	14		

CONCENTRATION of 57 elements in seawater is given in this table. Only sodium chloride (common salt), magnesium and bromine are now being extracted in significant amounts.

88 EDWARD WENK, JR.

They are widely distributed, with concentrations of 31,000 tons per square mile on the floor of the Pacific Ocean. Although commonly found at depths greater than 12,500 feet, nodules exist in 1,000 feet of water on the Blake Plateau off the southeastern U.S. and were located last year at a depth of 200 feet in the Great Lakes.

The nodules average about 24 percent manganese, 14 percent iron, 1 percent nickel, .5 percent copper and somewhat less than .5 percent cobalt. Since ore now being mined from land deposits in a number of countries averages 35 to 55 percent manganese, it may be the minor constituents of the nodules, particularly copper, cobalt and nickel, that first prove to be attractive economically. Many experts think the key to profitable exploitation is the solution of a difficult metallurgical separation problem created by the unique combination of minerals in the nodules.

Few discoveries have created more excitement among earth scientists than the location, by different expeditions in 1964, 1965 and 1966, of three undersea pools of hot, high-density brines in the middle of the Red Sea. The brines contain minerals in concentrations as high as 300,000 parts per million—nearly 10 times as much solid matter as is commonly dissolved in ocean water—and overlie sediments rich in such heavy metals as zinc, copper, lead, silver and gold. Similar deposits may be characteristic of other enclosed basins associated, as is the Red Sea, with rift valleys.

As this decade ends resource exploration is advancing on many fronts. Chromite has been found by Russian oceanographers in sea-floor rifts in the Indian Ocean, and zirconium, titanium and other heavy minerals have been detected in sediments from extensive areas off the Texas coast. Methane deposits sufficient to supply Italy's needs for at least six years have been confirmed in the Adriatic Sea. New oil fields of economic value have been discovered off Mexico, Trinidad, Brazil, Dahomey and Australia. Surveys of the Yellow Sea and the East China Sea indicate that the continental shelf between Taiwan and Japan may contain one of the richest oil reserves in the world. It is now becoming clear that the continental rises, which lie at depths ranging from about 5,000 to 18,000 feet and contain a far larger total volume of sediments than the shelves, may hold significant petroleum reserves. Within the past year the *Glomar Challenger* has drilled into oil-bearing sediments lying under 11,700 feet of water in the

Gulf of Mexico, and seismic surveys have revealed what appear to be typical oil-bearing structures under the deep ocean-basin floor [*see upper illustration on page 86*].

As on land, resource development of a frontier requires a mixture of public and private entrepreneurship. Historically basic exploration has been sponsored by government; this broad-ranging exploration reveals opportunities that are followed up by detailed privately funded surveys. This pattern is likely to persist, and as the International Decade of Ocean Exploration gets under way a wide variety of new opportunities

for marine resource development will surely come to light.

Limitations on the exploitation of the oceans stem partly from lack of knowledge about the distribution of resources and the state of the art of undersea technology. The major limits, however, are set by venture economics, the motivating factor for the profit sector. That factor is influenced by the availability of competing land deposits, by extraction technology and the legal situation and, most critically, by market demand. On the basis of projections of world population and gross national products to the year 2000, which indicate respective in-

CURRENT PRODUCTION of major ocean resources (except sand, gravel and shell) is mapped with areas of oil and gas exploration. Data come from U.S. Geological Survey, *Oil &*

creases of almost 100 and 500 percent over 1965, a sharp rise in total resource demand can be anticipated, and with it a greater role for the sea.

Other major impediments to the rapid development of ocean resources arise from social and legal constraints. Damage to beaches and wildlife from oil leaks, as in the Santa Barbara Channel, and uncertainty about the effect of dredging on marine organisms have brought public awareness that offshore development may have detrimental consequences. The public, the owner of the resources, is demanding greater safeguards, questioning the wisdom of re-

source development in areas where it may threaten the environment. In deeper waters seabed development comes up against the potent issue of ownership. There are major questions about the boundaries of national jurisdictions and about the jurisdiction over the seabed beyond such boundaries [see "The Ocean and Man," by Warren S. Wooster, page 121].

The coastal margin—the ribbon of land and water where people and oceans meet and are profoundly influenced by each other—has only recently come to be recognized and treated as a valuable and

perishable resource. It is actually a complex of unique physical resources: estuaries and lagoons, marshes, beaches and cliffs, bays and harbors, islands and spits and peninsulas.

In the year 2000 half of the estimated 312-million population of the U.S. will live on 5 percent of the land area in three coastal urban belts: the megalopolises of the Atlantic, the Pacific and the Great Lakes. Along with the people will come an intensification of competing demands for the limited resources of the narrow, fragile coastal zone. To make matters worse, the coastal resource is shrinking under the pressure of natural forces (hur-

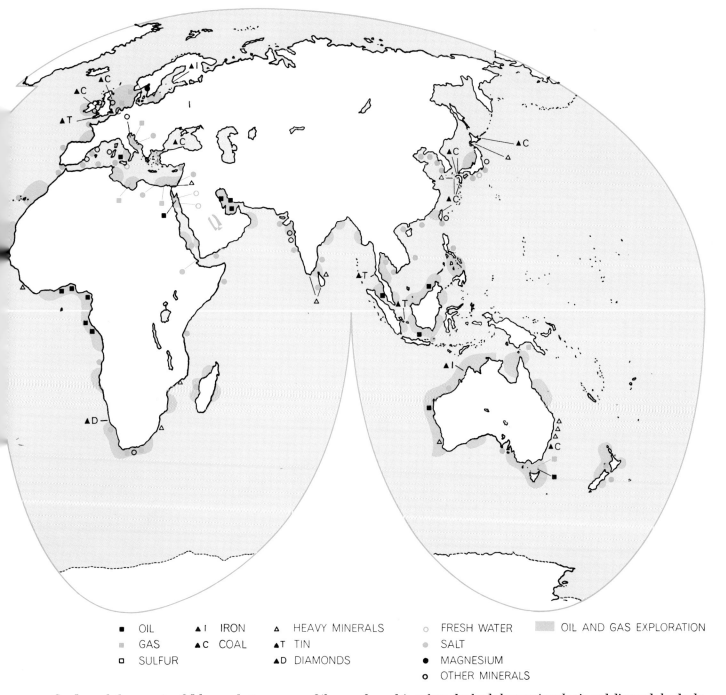

■	OIL	▲I IRON	△ HEAVY MINERALS	○ FRESH WATER		OIL AND GAS EXPLORATION
▪	GAS	▲C COAL	▲T TIN	• SALT		
□	SULFUR	▲D DIAMONDS	● MAGNESIUM			
			○ OTHER MINERALS			

Gas Journal, the magazine *Offshore* and other sources. Oil, gas and sulfur are produced by drilling; coal and iron ore from mines driven from dry land; heavy minerals, tin and diamonds by dredging; fresh water, salt, magnesium and other minerals from seawater.

MANGANESE NODULES, formed by precipitation from seawater, are generally found on the deep-sea floor. These nodules were photographed on the Blake Plateau off the southeastern U.S., less than 3,000 feet deep, by a prospecting ship operated by Deepsea Ventures, Inc. They average two inches in diameter, about a quarter-pound in weight. The manganese content is between 15 and 30 percent, the nickel and copper content about 1 percent each.

ricanes have caused $5 billion in damage to the U.S. economy in the past 15 years) and human exploitation and neglect.

More than a tenth of the 10.7 million square miles of shellfish-producing waters bordering the U.S. is now unusable because of pollution. Dredging, drainage projects and even chemical mosquito-control programs are having devastating effects on fish and other aquatic life. The amount of industrial waste reaching the oceans will increase sevenfold within the decade. Whereas 14 nuclear-powered generating plants are operating in the U.S. today, more than 100 are scheduled by 1975, with nine planned for Long Island Sound alone. Thermal pollution from the discharge of hot water is therefore a potential threat to coastal waters as well as inland lakes and rivers.

In the competition for the zone's resources among different uses—industrial and housing development, ports, shipbuilding, recreation, commercial fisheries and waste disposal—natural wetlands and estuarine open spaces are losing out. Of the tidal wetlands along the Atlantic coast from Maine to Delaware, 45,000 acres were lost between 1955 and 1964. An inventory shows that 34 percent of that area was dried up by being used as a dumping ground for dredging operations; 27 percent was filled for housing developments; 15 percent went to recreational developments (parks, beaches and marinas) and 10 percent to bridges, roads, parking lots and airports; 7 percent was turned into industrial sites and 6 percent into garbage and trash dumps. (In Maryland 176 acres of submerged

land in Chesapeake Bay were sold recently for $100 an acre and, after being filled with dredged bay-bottom muck, were subdivided into lots selling for between $4,000 and $8,000 each.)

With the demand for marine recreation growing with the coastal population, pressure is increasing on the one-third of the coastal zone that has recreational potential. Only about 6.5 percent of this is now in public ownership, yet in order to meet the projected demand it is considered essential that about 15 percent be accessible to the public. The mere fact that coastal land with recreational potential exists, moreover, is far from meaning that it will ever be put to recreational use. Swimming, boating and skin diving are often incompatible with competing alternative uses, many of which appear to have equally valid claims. In the face of conflicts between public and private, and long-term and short-term, benefits, how and by whom will the ultimate decisions be made on the proper utilization of coastal land?

Management of the coastal zone is unwieldy because the environment is almost hopelessly fragmented by political subdivisions: 24 states, more than 240 counties, some 600 coastal cities, townships, towns and villages and numerous regional authorities and special districts with their own regulatory powers. Superimposed on the many public jurisdictions there is another tapestry of private ownership. Because the states hold coastal resources in trust out to the three-mile limit, the Federal Government has a restricted role in resolving disputes, but it may be able to exert leadership in defining the issues.

Thoreau once admonished: "What is the use of a house if you haven't got a tolerable planet to put it on." Unless rational alternatives among competing uses are evaluated, the trend will continue to be toward single-purpose uses, motivated by short-term advantages to individuals, industry or local governments. Such exploitation may actually dissipate resources. Private beach development restricts public access; dredging and filling downgrade commercial fishing; offshore drilling rigs limit freedom of navigation. Each single-purpose use may seem justifiable on its own, but the overall effect of piecemeal development can be chaos.

In this technological age man can do many more of the things he wants to do. The oceans place before him a vast store of little-developed material resources; the tools of science and technology are at his disposal. This combination of a new frontier, new knowledge and new technical capability may be unique in the human experience. We are accumulating the basic information with which to define the ecological base from which we operate, to understand the natural forces at work and to predict the consequences of each insult to the environment. With this new comprehension it will soon be possible to develop the engineering with which to harvest mineral wealth, maintain water quality, inhibit beach erosion, create modern ports and harbors—and to establish the criteria for making necessary choices among courses of action and the law and institutions to effectuate them. In time we may even be able to correct mistakes that were made long ago in ignorance or that occur in the future because of man's stupidity, neglect or greed.

TIDAL WETLANDS, an important coastal resource, are disappearing rapidly. The top photograph shows Boca Ciega Bay, near St. Petersburg on the west coast of Florida, as it was in 1949. The bottom photograph shows the same area filled and developed, in 1969.

266684

VIII

The Food Resources of the Ocean

The Food Resources of the Ocean

S. J. HOLT

The present harvest of the oceans is roughly 55 million tons a year, half of which is consumed directly and half converted into fish meal. A well-managed world fishery could yield more than 200 million tons

I suppose we shall never know what was man's first use of the ocean. It may have been as a medium of transport or as a source of food. It is certain, however, that from early times up to the present the most important human uses of the ocean have been these same two: shipping and fishing. Today, when so much is being said and written about our new interests in the ocean, it is particularly important to retain our perspective. The annual income to the world's fishermen from marine catches is now roughly $8 billion. The world ocean-freight bill is nearly twice that. In contrast, the wellhead value of oil and gas from the seabed is barely half the value of the fish catch, and all the other ocean mineral production adds little more than another $250 million.

Of course, the present pattern is likely to change, although how rapidly or dramatically we do not know. What is certain is that we shall use the ocean more intensively and in a greater variety of ways. Our greatest need is to use it wisely. This necessarily means that we use it in a regulated way, so that each ocean resource, according to its nature, is efficiently exploited but also conserved. Such regulation must be in large measure of an international kind, particularly insofar as living resources are concerned. This will be so whatever may be the eventual legal regime of the high seas and the underlying bed. The obvious fact about most of the ocean's living resources is their mobility. For the most part they are lively animals, caring nothing about the lines we draw on charts.

The general goal of ecological research, to which marine biology makes an important contribution, is to achieve an understanding of and to turn to our advantage all the biological processes that give our planet its special character. Marine biology is focused on the prob-

lems of biological production, which are closely related to the problems of production in the economic sense. Our most compelling interest is narrower. It lies in ocean life as a renewable resource: primarily of protein-rich foods and food supplements for ourselves and our domestic animals, and secondarily of materials and drugs. I hope to show how in this field science, industry and government need each other now and will do so even more in the future. First, however, let me establish some facts about present fishing industries, the state of the art governing them and the state of the relevant science.

The present ocean harvest is about 55 million metric tons per year. More than 90 percent of this harvest is finfish; the rest consists of whales, crustaceans and mollusks and some other invertebrates. Although significant catches are reported by virtually all coastal countries, three-quarters of the total harvest is taken by only 14 countries, each of which produces more than a million tons annually and some much more. In the century from 1850 to 1950 the world catch increased tenfold—an average rate of about 25 percent per decade. In the next decade it nearly doubled, and this rapid growth is continuing [*see illustration on page 99*]. It is now a commonplace that fish is one of the few major foodstuffs showing an increase in global production that continues to exceed the growth rate of the human population.

This increase has been accompanied

by a changing pattern of use. Although some products of high unit value as luxury foods, such as shellfish, have maintained or even enhanced their relative economic importance, the trend has been for less of the catch to be used directly as human food and for more to be reduced to meal for animal feed. Just before World War II less than 10 percent of the world catch was turned into meal; by 1967 half of it was so used. Over the same period the proportion of the catch preserved by drying or smoking declined from 28 to 13 percent and the proportion sold fresh from 53 to 31 percent. The relative consumption of canned fish has hardly changed but that of frozen fish has grown from practically nothing to 12 percent.

While we are comparing the prewar or immediate postwar situation with the present, we might take a look at the composition of the catch by groups of species. In 1948 the clupeoid fishes (herrings, pilchards, anchovies and so on), which live mainly in the upper levels of the ocean, already dominated the scene (33 percent of the total by weight) and provided most of the material for fish meal. Today they bulk even larger (45 percent) in spite of the decline of several great stocks of them (in the North Sea and off California, for example). The next most important group, the gadoid fishes (cod, haddock, hake and so on), which live mainly on or near the bottom, comprised a quarter of the total in 1948. Although the catch of these fishes has continued to increase absolutely, the

SCHOOL OF FISH is spotted from the air at night by detecting the bioluminescent glow caused by the school's movement through the water. As the survey aircraft flew over the Gulf of Mexico at an altitude of 3,500 feet, the faint illumination in the water was amplified some 55,000 times by an image intensifier before appearing on the television screen seen in the photograph on the opposite page. The fish are Atlantic thread herring. Detection of fish from the air is one of several means of increasing fishery efficiency being tested at the Pascagoula, Miss., research base of the U.S. Bureau of Commercial Fisheries.

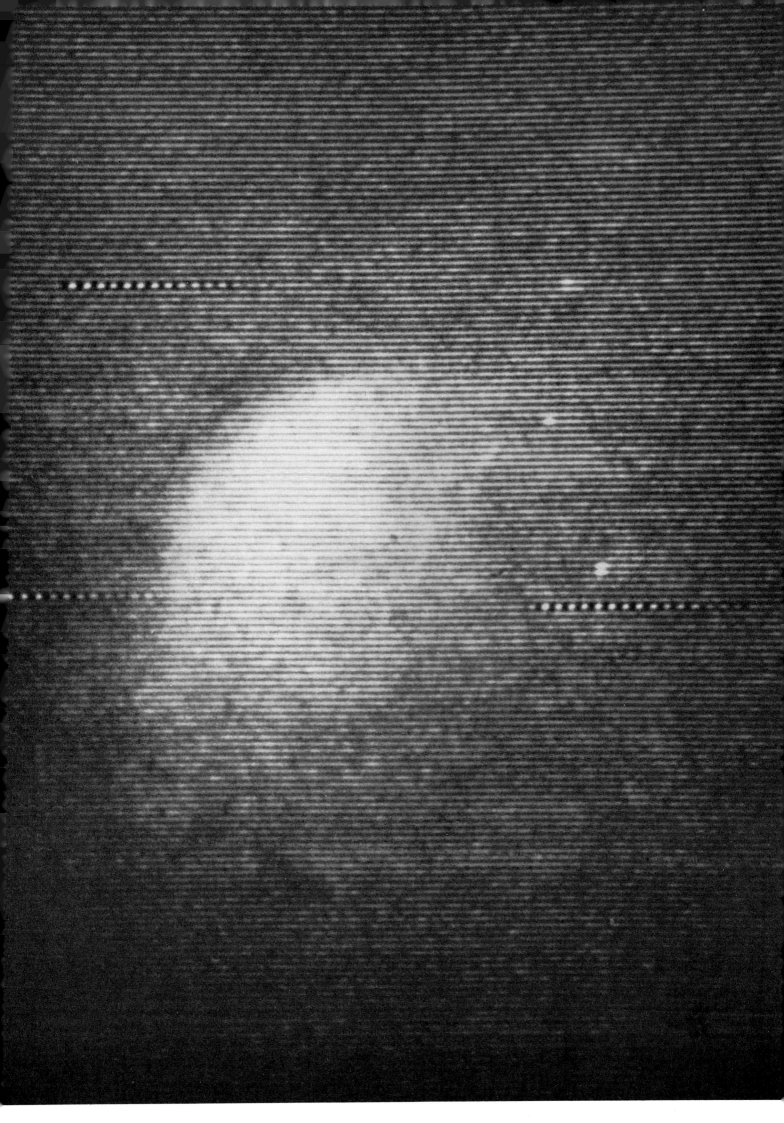

proportion is now reduced to 15 percent. The flounders and other flatfishes, the rosefish and other sea perches and the mullets and jacks have collectively stayed at about 15 percent; the tunas and mackerels, at 7 percent. Nearly a fifth of the total catch continues to be recorded in statistics as "Unsorted and other"—a vast number of species and groups, each contributing a small amount to a considerable whole.

The rise of shrimp and fish meal production together account for another major trend in the pattern of fisheries development. A fifth of the 1957 catch was sold in foreign markets; by 1967, two-fifths were entering international trade and export values totaled $2.5 billion.

Furthermore, during this same period the participation of the less developed countries in the export trade grew from a sixth to well over 25 percent. Most of these shipments were destined for markets in the richer countries, particularly shrimp for North America and fish meal for North America, Europe and Japan. More recently several of the less developed countries have also become importers of fish meal, for example Mexico and Venezuela, South Korea and the Republic of China.

The U.S. catch has stayed for many years in the region of two million tons, a low figure considering the size of the country, the length of the coastline and the ready accessibility of large resources

on the Atlantic, Gulf and Pacific sea-boards. The high level of consumption in the U.S. (about 70 pounds per capita) has been achieved through a steady growth in imports of fish and fish meal: from 25 percent of the total in 1950 to more than 70 percent in 1967. In North America 6 percent of the world's human population uses 12 percent of the world's catch, yet fishermen other than Americans take nearly twice the amount of fish that Americans take from the waters most readily accessible to the U.S.

There has not been a marked change in the broad geography of fishing [see illustration on these two pages]. The Pacific Ocean provides the biggest

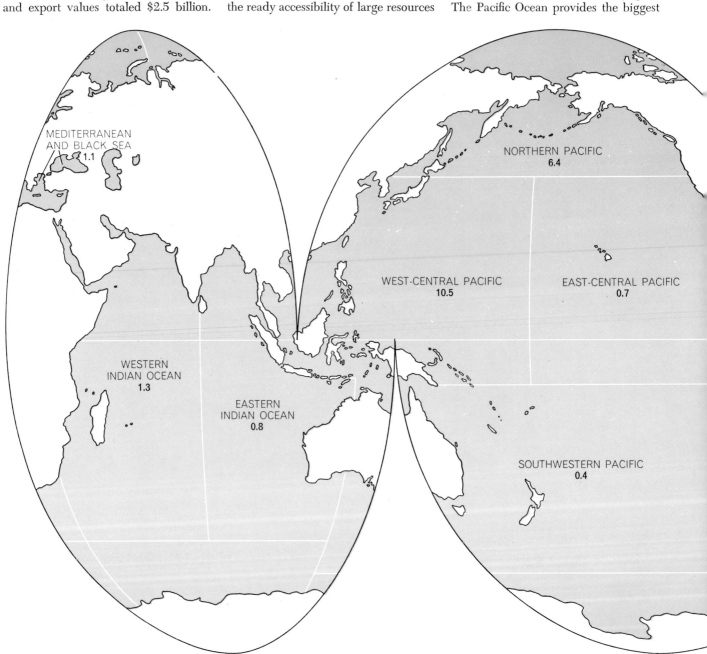

MAJOR MARINE FISHERY AREAS are 14 in number: two in the Indian Ocean (left), five in the Pacific Ocean (center) and six in the Atlantic (right). Due to the phenomenal expansion of the Peru fishery, the total Pacific yield is now a third larger than the Atlantic total. The bulk of Atlantic and Pacific catches, however, is still taken well north of the Equator. The Indian Ocean, with a

share (53 percent) but the Atlantic (40 percent, to which we may add 2 percent for the Mediterranean) is yielding considerably more per unit area. The Indian Ocean is still the source of less than 5 percent of the catch, and since it is not a biologically poor ocean it is an obvious target for future development. Within the major ocean areas, however, there have been significant changes. In the Pacific particular areas such as the waters off Peru and Chile and the Gulf of Thailand have rapidly acquired importance. The central and southern parts of the Atlantic, both east and west, are of growing interest to more nations. Although, with certain exceptions, the traditional fisheries in the colder waters of the Northern Hemisphere still dominate the statistics, the emergence of some of the less developed countries as modern fishing nations and the introduction of long-range fleets mean that tropical and subtropical waters are beginning to contribute significantly to world production.

Finally, in this brief review of the trends of the past decade or so we must mention the changing importance of countries as fishing powers. Peru has become the leading country in terms of sheer magnitude of catch (although not of value or diversity) through the development of the world's greatest one-species fishery: 10 million tons of anchovies per year, almost all of which is reduced to meal [*see illustration on page 101*].

The U.S.S.R. has also emerged as a fishing power of global dimension, fishing for a large variety of products throughout the oceans of the world, particularly with large factory ships and freezer-trawlers.

At this point it is time to inquire about the future expectations of the ocean as a major source of protein. In spite of the growth I have described, fisheries still contribute only a tenth of the animal protein in our diet, although this proportion varies considerably from one part of the world to another. Before such an inquiry can be pursued, however, it is necessary to say something about the problem of overfishing.

A stock of fish is, generally speaking, at its most abundant when it is not being exploited; in that virgin state it will include a relatively high proportion of the larger and older individuals of the species. Every year a number of young recruits enter the stock, and all the fish—but particularly the younger ones—put on weight. This overall growth is balanced by the natural death of fish of all ages from disease, predation and perhaps senility. When fishing begins, the large stock yields large catches to each fishing vessel, but because the pioneering vessels are few, the total catch is small.

Increased fishing tends to reduce the level of abundance of the stock progressively. At these reduced levels the losses accountable to "natural" death will be less than the gains accountable to recruitment and individual growth. If, then, the catch is less than the difference between natural gains and losses, the stock will tend to increase again; if the catch is more, the stock will decrease. When the stock neither decreases nor increases, we achieve a sustained yield. This sustained yield is small when the stock is large and also when the stock is small; it is at its greatest when the stock is at an intermediate level—somewhere between two-thirds and one-third of the virgin abundance. In this intermediate stage the average size of the individuals will be smaller and the age will be younger than in the unfished condition, and individual growth will be highest in relation to the natural mortality.

The largest catch that on the average can be taken year after year without causing a shift in abundance, either up or down, is called the maximum sustainable yield. It can best be obtained by leaving the younger fish alone and fishing the older ones heavily, but we can also get near to it by fishing moderately, taking fish of all sizes and ages. This

NORTHWESTERN ATLANTIC 4.0

NORTHEASTERN ATLANTIC 10.2

WEST-CENTRAL ATLANTIC 1.3

EAST-CENTRAL ATLANTIC 1.6

SOUTHEASTERN PACIFIC 11.2

SOUTHWESTERN ATLANTIC 1.3

SOUTHEASTERN ATLANTIC 2.5

total catch of little more than two million metric tons, live weight, is the world's major underexploited region. The number below each area name shows the millions of metric tons landed during 1967, as reported by the UN Food and Agriculture Organization.

phenomenon—catches that first increase and then decrease as the intensity of fishing increases—does not depend on any correlation between the number of parent fish and the number of recruits they produce for the following generation. In fact, many kinds of fish lay so many eggs, and the factors governing survival of the eggs to the recruit stage are so many and so complex, that it is not easy to observe any dependence of the number of recruits on the number of their parents over a wide range of stock levels.

Only when fishing is intense, and the stock is accordingly reduced to a small fraction of its virgin size, do we see a decline in the number of recruits coming in each year. Even then there is often a wide annual fluctuation in this number. Indeed, such fluctuation, which causes the stock as a whole to vary greatly in abundance from year to year, is one of the most significant characteristics of living marine resources. Fluctuation in number, together with the considerable variation in "availability" (the change in the geographic location of the fish with respect to the normal fishing area), largely account for the notorious riskiness of fishing as an industry.

For some species the characteristics of growth, natural mortality and recruit-

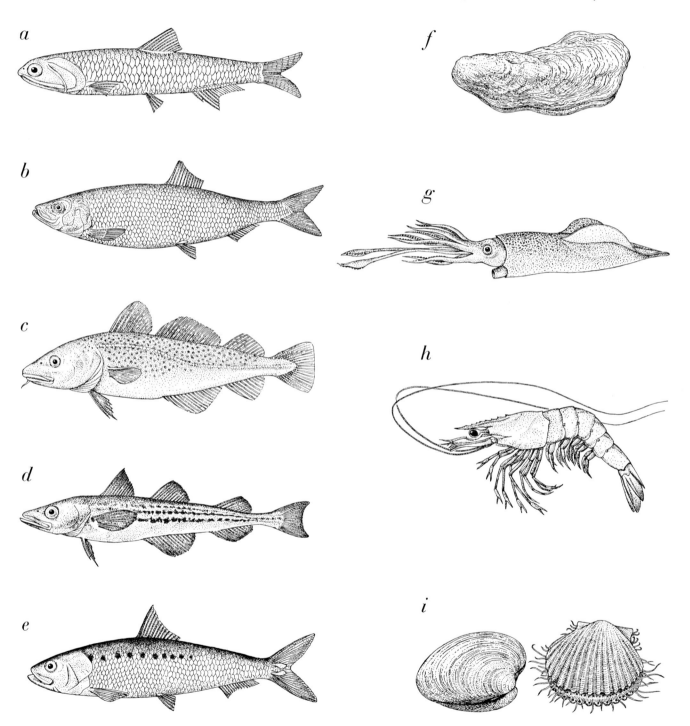

LARGEST CATCHES of individual fish species include the five fishes shown here (left). They are, according to the most recent detailed FAO fishery statistics (1967), the Peruvian anchoveta (a), with a catch of more than 10.5 million metric tons; the Atlantic herring (b), with a catch of more than 3.8 million tons; the Atlantic cod (c), with a catch of 3.1 million tons; the Alaska walleye pollack (d), with a catch of 1.7 million metric tons, and the South African pilchard (e), with a catch of 1.1 million tons. No single invertebrate species (right) is harvested in similar quantities. Taken as a group, however, various oyster species (f) totaled .83 million tons in 1967; squids (g), .75 million tons; shrimps and prawns (h), .69 million tons; clams and cockles (i), .48 million tons.

ment are such that the maximum sustainable yield is sharply defined. The catch will decline quite steeply with a change in the amount of fishing (measured in terms of the number of vessels, the tonnage of the fleet, the days spent at sea or other appropriate index) to either below or above an optimum. In other species the maximum is not so sharply defined; as fishing intensifies above an optimum level the sustained catch will not significantly decline, but it will not rise much either.

Such differences in the dynamics of different types of fish stock contribute to the differences in the historical development of various fisheries. If it is unregulated, however, each fishery tends to expand beyond its optimum point unless something such as inadequate demand hinders its expansion. The reason is painfully simple. It will usually still be profitable for an individual fisherman or ship to continue fishing after the *total* catch from the stock is no longer increasing or is declining, and even though his own rate of catch may also be declining. By the same token, it may continue to be profitable for the individual fisherman to use a small-meshed net and thereby catch young as well as older fish, but in doing so he will reduce both his own possible catch and that of others in future years. Naturally if the total catch is declining, or not increasing much, as the amount of fishing continues to increase, the net economic yield from the fishery—that is, the difference between the total costs of fishing and the value of the entire catch—will be well past its maximum. The well-known case of the decline of the Antarctic baleen whales provides a dramatic example of overfishing and, one would hope, a strong incentive for the more rational conduct of ocean fisheries in the future.

There is, then, a limit to the amount that can be taken year after year from each natural stock of fish. The extent to which we can expect to increase our fish catches in the future will depend on three considerations. First, how many as yet unfished stocks await exploitation, and how big are they in terms of potential sustainable yield? Second, how many of the stocks on which the existing fisheries are based are already reaching or have passed their limit of yield? Third, how successful will we be in managing our fisheries to ensure maximum sustainable yields from the stocks?

The first major conference to examine the state of marine fish stocks on a global basis was the United Nations Scientific Conference on the Conservation and Utilization of Resources, held in 1949 at Lake Success, N.Y. The small group of fishery scientists gathered there concluded that the only overfished stocks at that time were those of a few high-priced species in the North Atlantic and North Pacific, particularly plaice, halibut and salmon. They produced a map showing 30 other known major stocks they believed to be underfished. The situation was reexamined in 1968. Fishing on half of those 30 stocks is now close to or beyond that required for maximum yield. The fully fished or overfished stocks include some tunas in most ocean areas, the herring, the cod and ocean perch in the North Atlantic and the anchovy in the southeastern Pacific. The point is that the history of development of a fishery from small beginnings to the stage of full utilization or overutilization can, in the modern world, be compressed into a very few years. This happened with the anchovy off Peru, as a result of a massive local fishery growth, and it has happened to some demersal, or bottom-dwelling, fishes elsewhere through the large-scale redeployment of long-distance trawlers from one ocean area to another.

It is clear that the classical process of fleets moving from an overfished area to another area, usually more distant and less fished, cannot continue indefinitely. It is true that since the Lake Success

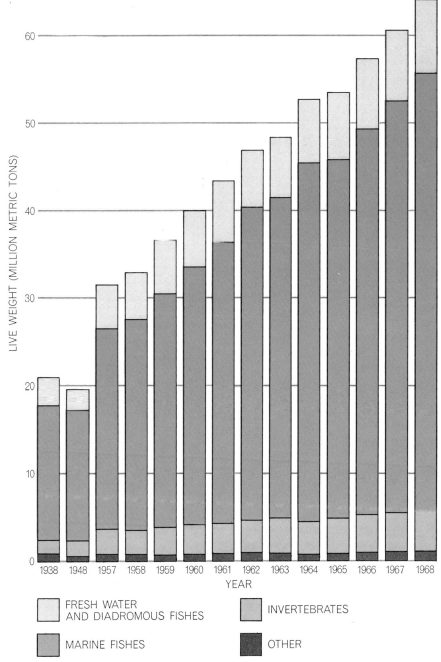

WORLD FISH CATCH has more than tripled in the three decades since 1938; the FAO estimate of the 1968 total is 64 million metric tons. The largest part consists of marine fishes. Humans directly consume only half of the catch; the rest becomes livestock feed.

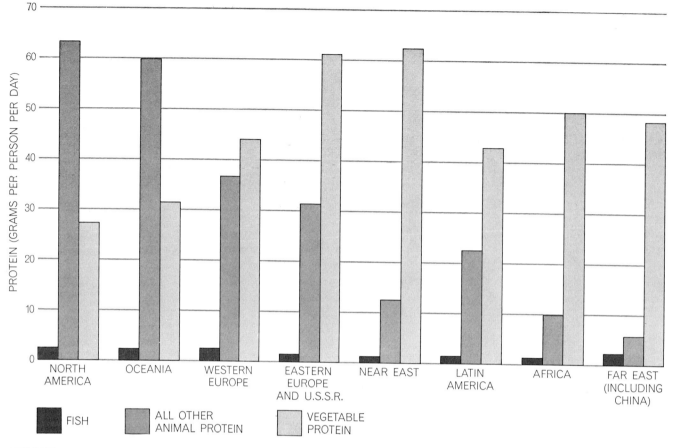

PROTEIN (GRAMS PER PERSON PER DAY)

FISH
ALL OTHER ANIMAL PROTEIN
VEGETABLE PROTEIN

RELATIVELY MINOR ROLE played by fish in the world's total consumption of protein is apparent when the grams of fish eaten per person per day in various parts of the world (*left column in each group*) is compared with the consumption of other animal protein (*middle column*) and vegetable protein (*right column*). The supply is nonetheless growing more rapidly than world population.

meeting several other large resources have been discovered, mostly in the Indian Ocean and the eastern Pacific, and additional stocks have been utilized in fishing areas with a long history of intensive fishing, such as the North Sea. In another 20 years, however, very few substantial stocks of fish of the kinds and sizes of commercial interest and accessible to the fishing methods we know now will remain underexploited.

The Food and Agriculture Organization of the UN is now in the later stages of preparing what is known as its Indicative World Plan (IWP) for agricultural development. Under this plan an attempt is being made to forecast the production of foodstuffs in the years 1975 and 1985. For fisheries this involves appraising resource potential, envisioning technological changes and their consequences, and predicting demand. The latter predictions are not yet available, but the resource appraisals are well advanced. With the cooperation of a large number of scientists and organizations estimates are being prepared in great detail on an area basis. They deal with the potential of known stocks, both those fished actively at present and those

exploited little or not at all. Some of these estimates are reliable; others are naturally little more than reasonable guesses. One fact is abundantly clear: We still have very scrappy knowledge, in quantitative terms, of the living resources of the ocean. We can, however, check orders of magnitude by comparing the results of different methods of appraisal. Thus where there is good information on the growth and mortality rates of fishes and measures of their numbers in absolute terms, quite good projections can be made. Most types of fish can now in fact virtually be counted individually by the use of specially calibrated echo sounders for area surveys, although this technique is not yet widely applied. The size of fish populations can also be deduced from catch statistics, from measurements of age based on growth rings in fish scales or bands in fish ear stones, and from tagging experiments. Counts and maps of the distribution of fish eggs in the plankton can in some cases give us a fair idea of fish abundance in relative terms. We can try to predict the future catch in an area little fished at present by comparing the present catch with the catch in another area that has similar oceanographic char-

acteristics and basic biological productivity and that is already yielding near its maximum. Finally, we have estimates of the food supply available to the fish in a particular area, or of the primary production there, and from what we know about metabolic and ecological efficiency we can try to deduce fish production.

So far as the data permit these methods are being applied to major groups of fishes area by area. Although individual area and group predictions will not all be reliable, the global totals and subtotals may be. The best figure seems to be that the potential catch is about three times the present one; it might be as little as twice or as much as four times. A similar range has been given in estimates of the potential yield from waters adjacent to the U.S.: 20 million tons compared with the present catch of rather less than six million tons. This is more than enough to meet the U.S. demand, which is expected to reach 10 million tons by 1975 and 12 million by 1985.

Judging from the rate of fishery development in the recent past, it would be entirely reasonable to suppose that the maximum sustainable world catch of between 100 and 200 million tons could be reached by the second IWP target date, 1985, or at least by the end of the century. The real question is whether or not this will be economically worth the effort. Here any forecast is, in my view, on soft ground. First, to double the catch we have to more than double the amount of fishing, because the stocks decline in abundance as they are exploited. Moreover, as we approach the global maximum more of the stocks that are lightly fished at present will be brought down to intermediate levels. Second, fishing will become even more competitive and costly if the nations fail to agree, and agree soon, on regulations to cure overfishing situations. Third, it is quite uncertain what will happen in the long run to the costs of production and the price of protein of marine origin in relation to other protein sources, particularly from mineral or vegetable bases.

In putting forward these arguments I am not trying to damp enthusiasm for the sea as a major source of food for coming generations; quite the contrary. I do insist, however, that it would be dangerous for those of us who are interested in such development to assume that past growth will be maintained along familiar lines. We need to rationalize present types of fishing while preparing ourselves actively for a "great leap forward." Fishing as we now know it will need to be made even more efficient; we shall need to consider the direct use of the smaller organisms in the ocean that mostly constitute the diet of the fish we now catch; we shall need to try harder to improve on nature by breeding, rearing and husbanding useful marine animals and cultivating their pasture. To achieve this will require a much larger scale and range of scientific research, wedded to engineering progress; expansion by perhaps an order of magnitude in investment and in the employment of highly skilled labor, and a modified legal regime for the ocean and its bed not only to protect the investments but also to ensure orderly development and provide for the safety of men and their installations.

To many people the improvement of present fishing activities will mean increasing the efficiency of fishing gear and ships. There is surely much that could be done to this end. We are only just beginning to understand how trawls, traps, lines and seines really work. For example, every few years someone tries a new design or rigging for a deep-sea trawl, often based on sound engineering and hydrodynamic studies. Rarely do these "improved" rigs catch more than the old ones; sometimes they catch much

less. The error has been in thinking that the trawl is simply a bag, collecting more or less passive fish, or at least predictably active ones. This is not so at all. We really have to deal with a complex, dynamic relation between the lively animals and their environment, which includes in addition to the physical and biological environment the fishing gear itself. We can expect success in understanding and exploiting this relation now that we can telemeter the fishing gear, study its hydrodynamics at full scale as well as with models in towing tanks, monitor it (and the fish) by means of underwater television, acoustic equipment and divers, and observe and experiment with fish behavior both in the sea and in large tanks. We also probably have something to learn from studying, before they become extinct, some kinds of traditional "primitive" fishing gear still used in Asia, South America and elsewhere—mainly traps that take advantage of subtleties of fish behavior observed over many centuries.

Successful fishing depends not so much on the size of fish stocks as on their concentration in space and time. All fishermen use knowledge of such concentrations; they catch fish where they have

gathered to feed or to reproduce, or where they are on the move in streams or schools. Future fishing methods will surely involve a more active role for the fishermen in causing the fish to congregate. In many parts of the world lights or sound are already used to attract fish. We can expect more sophistication in the employment of these and other stimuli, alone and in combination.

Fishing operations as a whole also depend on locating areas of concentration and on the efficient prediction, or at least the prompt observation, of changes in these areas. The large stocks of pelagic, or open-sea, fishes are produced mainly in areas of "divergencies," where water is rising from deeper levels toward the surface and hence where surface waters are flowing outward. Many such areas are the "upwellings" off the western coasts of continental masses, for example off western and southwestern Africa, western India and western South America. Here seasonal winds, currents and continental configurations combine to cause a periodic enrichment of the surface waters.

Divergencies are also associated with

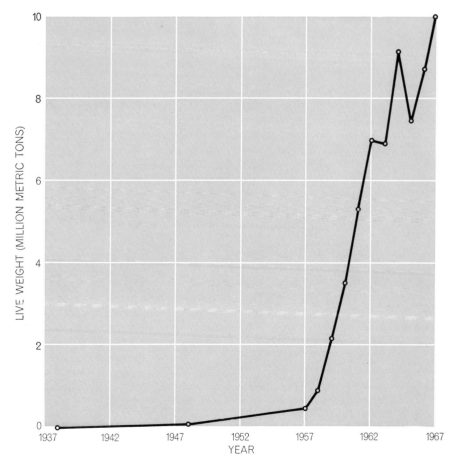

EXPLOSIVE GROWTH of the Peruvian anchoveta fishery is seen in rising number of fish taken between 1938 and 1967. Until 1958 the catch remained below half a million tons. By 1967, with more than 10.5 million tons taken, the fishery sorely needed management.

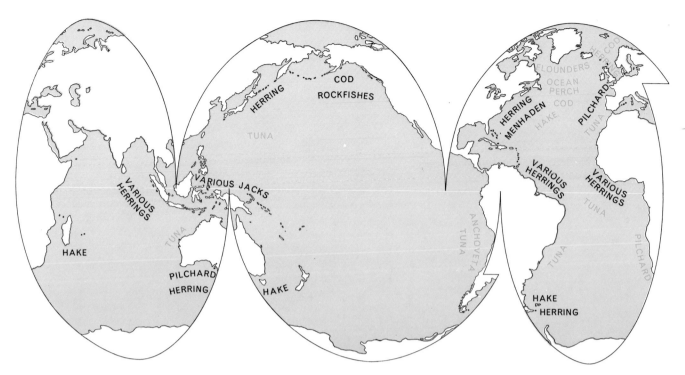

EXPLOITATION OF FISHERIES during the past 20 years is evident from this map, which locates 30 major fish stocks that were thought to be underfished in 1949. Today 14 of the stocks (*color*) are probably fully exploited or in danger of being overfished.

certain current systems in the open sea. The classical notion is that biological production is high in such areas because nutrient salts, needed for plant growth and in limited supply, are thereby renewed in the surface layers of the water. On the other hand, there is a view that the blooming of the phytoplankton is associated more with the fact that the water coming to the surface is cooler than it is associated with its richness in nutrients. A cool-water regime is characterized by seasonal peaks of primary production; the phytoplankton blooms are followed, after a time lag, by an abundance of herbivorous zooplankton that provides concentrations of food for large schools of fish. Fish, like fishermen, thrive best not so much where their prey are abundant as where they are most aggregated. In any event, the times and places of aggregation vary from year to year. The size of the herbivore crop also varies according to the success of synchronization with the primary production cycle.

There would be great practical advantage to our being able to predict these variations. Since the weather regime plays such a large part in creating the physical conditions for high biological production, the World Weather Watch, under the auspices of the World Meteorological Organization, should contribute much to fishery operations through both long-range forecasting and better short-term forecasting. Of course our interest is not merely in atmospheric forecasts,

nor in the state of the sea surface, but in the deeper interaction of atmosphere and ocean. Thus, from the point of view of fisheries, an equal and complementary partner in the World Weather Watch will be the Integrated Global Ocean Station System (IGOSS) now being developed by the Intergovernmental Oceanographic Commission. The IGOSS will give us the physical data, from networks of satellite-interrogated automatic buoys and other advanced ocean data acquisition systems (collectively called ODAS), by which the ocean circulation can be observed in "real time" and the parameters relevant to fisheries forecast. A last and much more difficult link will be the observation and prediction of the basic biological processes.

So far we have been considering mainly the stocks of pelagic fishes in the upper layers of the open ocean and the shallower waters over the continental shelves. There are also large aggregations of pelagic animals that live farther down and are associated particularly with the "deep scattering layer," the sound-reflecting stratum observed in all oceans. The more widespread use of submersible research vessels will tell us more about the layer's biological nature, but the exploitation of deep pelagic resources awaits the development of suitable fishing apparatus for this purpose.

Important advances have been made in recent years in the design of pelagic trawls and in means of guiding them in

three dimensions and "locking" them onto fish concentrations. We shall perhaps have such gear not only for fishing much more deeply than at present but also for automatically homing on deep-dwelling concentrations of fishes, squids and so on, using acoustic links for the purpose. The Indian Ocean might become the part of the world where such methods are first deployed on a large scale; certainly there is evidence of a great but scarcely utilized pelagic resource in that ocean, and around its edge are human populations sorely in need of protein. The Gulf of Guinea is another place where oceanographic knowledge and new fishing methods should make accessible more of the large sardine stock that is now effectively exploited only during the short season of upwelling off Ghana and nearby countries, when the schools come near the surface and can be taken by purse seines.

The bottom-living fishes and the shellfishes (both mollusks and crustaceans) are already more fully utilized than the smaller pelagic fishes. On the whole they are the species to which man attaches a particularly high value, but they cannot have as high a global abundance as the pelagic fishes. The reason is that they are living at the end of a longer food chain. All the rest of ocean life depends on an annual primary production of 150 billion tons of phytoplankton in the 2 to 3 percent of the water mass into which light penetrates and photosynthesis can occur. Below this "photic" zone dead and dying organisms sink as a continual rain of organic matter and are eaten or decompose. Out in the deep ocean little, if any, of this organic matter reaches the bottom, but nearer land a substantial quantity does; it nourishes an entire community of marine life, the benthos, which itself provides food for animals such as cod, ocean perch, flounder and shrimp that dwell or visit there.

Thus virtually everywhere on the bed of the continental shelf there is a thriving demersal resource, but it does not end there. Where the shelf is narrow but primary production above is high, as in the upwelling areas, or where the zone of high primary production stretches well away from the coast, we may find considerable demersal resources on the continental slopes beyond the shelf, far deeper than the 200 meters that is the average limiting depth of the shelf itself. Present bottom-trawling methods will work down to 1,000 meters or more, and it seems that, at least on some slopes, useful resources of shrimps and bottom-dwelling fishes will be found even down to 1,500 meters. We still know very little about the nature and abundance of these resources, and current techniques of acoustic surveying are not of much use in evaluating them. The total area of the continental slope from, say, 200 to 1,500 meters is roughly the same as that of the entire continental shelf, so that when we have extended our preliminary surveys there we might need to revise our IWP ceiling upward somewhat.

Another problem is posed for us by the way that, as fishing is intensified throughout the world, it becomes at the same time less selective. This may not apply to a particular type of fishing operation, which may be highly selective with regard to the species captured. Partly as a result of the developments in processing and trade, and partly because of the decline of some species, however, we are using more and more of the species that abound. This holds particularly for species in warmer waters, and also for some species previously neglected in cool waters, such as the sand eel in the North Sea. This means that it is no longer so reasonable to calculate the potential of each important species stock separately, as we used to do. Instead we need new theoretical models for that part of the marine ecosystem which consists of animals in the wide range of sizes we now utilize: from an inch or so up to several feet. As we move toward fuller utilization of all these animals we shall need to take proper account of the interactions among them. This will mean devising quantitative methods for evaluat-

ing the competition among them for a common food supply and also examining the dynamic relations between the predators and the prey among them.

These changes in the degree and quality of exploitation will add one more dimension to the problems we already face in creating an effective international system of management of fishing activities, particularly on the high seas. This system consists at present of a large number—more than 20—of regional or specialized intergovernmental organizations established under bilateral or multilateral treaties, or under the constitution of the FAO. The purpose of each is to conduct and coordinate research leading to resource assessments, or to promulgate regulations for the better conduct of the fisheries, or both. The organizations are supplemented by the 1958 Geneva Convention on Fishing and Conservation of the Living Resources of the High Seas. The oldest of them, the International Council for the Exploration of the Sea, based in Copenhagen and concerned particularly with fishery research in the northeastern Atlantic and the Arctic, has had more than half a century of activity. The youngest is the International Commission for the Conservation of Atlantic Tunas; the convention that establishes it comes into force this year.

For the past two decades many have hoped that such treaty bodies would en-

sure a smooth and reasonably rapid approach to an international regime for ocean fisheries. Indeed, a few of the organizations have fair successes to their credit. The fact is, however, that the fisheries have been changing faster than the international machinery to deal with them. National fishery research budgets and organizational arrangements for guiding research, collecting proper statistics and so on have been largely inadequate to the task of assessing resources. Nations have given, and continue to give, ludicrously low-level support to the bodies of which they are members, and the bodies themselves do not have the powers they need properly to manage the fisheries and conserve the resources. Add to this the trend to high mobility and range of today's fishing fleets, the problems of species interaction and the growing number of nations at various stages of economic development participating in international fisheries, and the regional bodies are indeed in trouble! There is some awareness of this, yet the FAO, having for years been unable to give adequate financial support to the fishery bodies it set up years ago in the Indo-Pacific area, the Mediterranean and the southwestern Atlantic, has been pushed, mainly through the enthusiasm of its new intergovernmental Committee on Fisheries, to establish still other bodies (in the Indian Ocean and in the east-central and southeastern Atlantic) that will be no better supported than the ex-

RUSSIAN FACTORY SHIP *Polar Star* lies hove to in the Barents Sea in June, 1968, as two vessels from its fleet of trawlers unload their catch for processing. The worldwide activities of the Russian fishing fleet have made the U.S.S.R. the third-largest fishing nation.

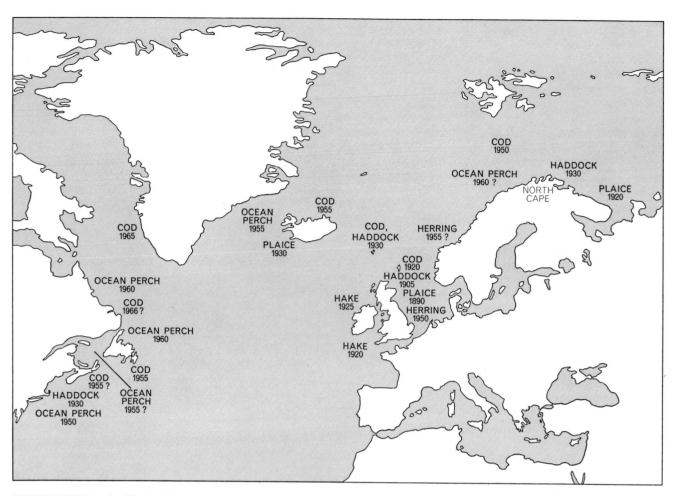

OVERFISHING in the North Atlantic and adjacent waters began some 80 years ago in the North Sea, when further increases in fishing the plaice stock no longer produced an increase in the catch of that fish. By 1950 the same was true of North Sea cod, haddock and herring, of cod, haddock and plaice off the North Cape and in the Barents Sea, of plaice, haddock and cod south and east of Iceland and of the ocean perch and haddock in the Gulf of Maine. In the period between 1956 and 1966 the same became true of ocean perch off Newfoundland and off Labrador and of cod west of Greenland. It may also be true of North Cape ocean perch and Labrador cod.

isting ones. A grand plan to double the finance and staff of the FAO's Department of Fisheries (including the secretariats and working budgets of the associated regional fishery bodies) over the six-year period 1966–1971, which member nations endorsed in principle in 1965, will be barely half-fulfilled in that time, and the various nations concerned are meanwhile being equally parsimonious in financing the other international fishery bodies.

Several of these bodies are now facing a crucial, and essentially political, problem: How are sustainable yields to be shared equitably among participating nations? It is now quite evident that there is really no escape from the paramount need, if high yields are to be sustained; this is to limit the fishing effort deployed in the intensive fisheries. This could be achieved by setting total quotas for each species in each type of fishery, but this only leads to an unseemly scramble by each nation for as large a share as possible of the quota. This can only be avoided by agreement on national al-

locations of the quotas. On what basis can such agreement be reached? On the historical trends of national participation? If so, over what period: the past two years, the past five, the past 20? On the need for protein, on the size or wealth of the population or on the proximity of coasts to fishing grounds? Might we try to devise a system for maximizing economic efficiency in securing an optimum net economic yield? How can this be measured in an international fishery? Would some form of license auction be equitable, or inevitably loaded in favor of wealthy nations? The total number or tonnage of fishing vessels might be fixed, as the United Kingdom suggested in 1946 should be done in the North Sea, but what flags should the ships fly and in what proportion? Might we even consider "internationalizing" the resources, granting fishing concessions and using at least a part of the economic yield from the concessions to finance marine research, develop fish-farming, police the seas and aid the participation of less developed nations?

Some of my scientific colleagues are optimistic about the outcome of current negotiations on these questions, and indeed when the countries participating are a handful of nations at a similar stage of economic and technical development, as was the case for Antarctic whaling, agreement can sometimes be reached by hard bargaining. What happens, however, when the participating countries are numerous, widely varying in their interests and ranging from the most powerful nations on earth to states most newly emerged to independence? I must confess that many of us were optimistic when 20 years ago we began proposing quite reasonable net-mesh regulations to conserve the young of certain fish stocks. Then we saw these simple—I suppose oversimple—ideas bog down in consideration of precisely how to measure a mesh of a particular kind of twine, and how to take account of the innumerable special situations that countries pleaded for, so that fishery research sometimes seemed to be becoming perverted from its earlier clarity and broad perspective.

Apprehension and doubt about the ultimate value of the concept of regulation through regional commissions of the present type have, I think, contributed to the interest in recent years in alternative regimes: either the "appropriation" of high-seas resources to some form of international "ownership" instead of today's condition of no ownership or, at the other extreme, the appropriation of increasingly wide ocean areas to national ownership by coastal states. As is well known, a similar dialectic is in progress in connection with the seabed and its mineral resources. Either solution would have both advantages and disadvantages, depending on one's viewpoint, on the time scale considered and on political philosophy. I do not propose to discuss these matters here, although personally I am increasingly firm in the conclusion that mankind has much more to gain in the long run from the "international" solution, with both seabed and fishery resources being considered as our common heritage. We now at least have a fair idea of what is economically at stake.

Here are some examples. The wasted effort in capture of cod alone in the northeastern Atlantic and salmon alone in the northern Pacific could, if rationally deployed elsewhere, increase the total world catch by 5 percent. The present catch of cod, valued at $350 million per year, could be taken with only half the effort currently expended, and the annual saving in fishing effort would amount to $150 million or more. The cost of harvesting salmon off the West Coast of North America could be reduced by three-quarters if management policy permitted use of the most efficient fishing gear; the introduction of such a policy would increase net economic returns by $750,000 annually.

The annual benefit that would accrue from the introduction and enforcement of mesh regulations in the demersal fishery—mainly the hake fishery—in the east-central Atlantic off West Africa is of the order of $1 million. Failure to regulate the Antarctic whaling industry effectively in earlier years, when stocks of blue whales and fin whales were near their optimum size, is now costing us tens of millions of dollars annually in loss of this valuable but only slowly renewable resource. Even under stringent regulation this loss will continue for the decades these stocks will need to recover. Yellowfin tuna in the eastern tropical Pacific are almost fully exploited. There is an annual catch quota, but it is not allocated to nations or ships, with the classic inevitable results: an increase in the catching capacity of fleets, their use in shorter and

shorter "open" seasons and an annual waste of perhaps 30 percent of the net value of this important fishery.

Such regulations as exist are extremely difficult to enforce (or to be seen to be enforced, which is almost as important). The tighter the squeeze on the natural resources, the greater the suspicion of fishermen that "the others" are not abiding by the regulations, and the greater the incentive to flout the regulations oneself. There has been occasional provision in treaties, or in *ad hoc* arrangements, to place neutral inspectors or internationally accredited observers aboard fishing vessels and mother ships (as in Antarctic whaling, where arrangements were completed but never implemented!). Such arrangements are exceptional. In point of fact the effective supervision of a fishing fleet is an enormously difficult undertaking. Even to know where the vessels are going, let alone what they are catching, is quite a problem. Perhaps one day artificial satellites will monitor sealed transmitters compulsorily carried on each vessel. But how to ensure compliance with minimum landing-size regulations when increasing quantities of the catch are being processed at sea? With factory ships roaming the entire ocean, even the statistics reporting catches by species and area can become more rather than less difficult to obtain.

Some of these considerations and pessimism about their early solution have, I think, played their part in stimulating other approaches to harvesting the sea.

One of these is the theory of "working back down the food chain." For every ton of fish we catch, the theory goes, we might instead catch say 10 tons of the organisms on which those fish feed. Thus by harvesting the smaller organisms we could move away from the fish ceiling of 100 million or 200 million tons and closer to the 150 billion tons of primary production. The snag is the question of concentration. The billion tons or so of "fish food" is neither in a form of direct interest to man nor is it so concentrated in space as the animals it nourishes. In fact, the 10-to-one ratio of fish food to fish represents a use of energy—perhaps a rather efficient use—by which biomass is concentrated; if the fish did not expend this energy in feeding, man might have to expend a similar amount of energy—in fuel, for example—in order to collect the dispersed fish food. I am sure the technological problems of our using fish food will be solved, but only careful analysis will reveal whether or not it is better to turn fish food, by way of fish meal, into chickens or rainbow trout than to harvest the marine fish instead.

There are a few situations, however, where the concentration, abundance and homogeneity of fish food are sufficient to be of interest in the near future. The best-known of these is the euphausiid "krill" in Antarctic waters: small shrimplike crustaceans that form the main food of the baleen whales. Russian investigators and some others are seriously charting krill distribution and production, relating them to the oceanographic features of the Southern Ocean, experiment-

JAPANESE MARICULTURE includes the raising of several kinds of marine algae. This array of posts and netting in the Inland Sea supports a crop of an edible seaweed, *Porphyra*.

AUSTRALIAN MARICULTURE includes the production of some 60 million oysters per year in the brackish estuaries of New South Wales. The long racks in the photograph have been exposed by low tide; they support thousands of sticks covered with maturing oysters.

ing with special gear for catching the krill (something between a mid-water trawl and a magnified plankton net) and developing methods for turning them into meal and acceptable pastes. The krill alone could produce a weight of yield, although surely not a value, at least as great as the present world fish catch, but we might have to forgo the whales. Similarly, the deep scattering layers in other oceans might provide very large quantities of smaller marine animals in harvestable concentration.

An approach opposite to working down the food chain is to look to the improvement of the natural fish resources, and particularly to the cultivation of highly valued species. Schemes for transplanting young fish to good high-seas feeding areas, or for increasing recruitment by rearing young fish to viable size, are hampered by the problem of protecting what would need to be quite large investments. What farmer would bother to breed domestic animals if he were not assured by the law of the land that others would not come and take them as soon as they were nicely fattened? Thus mariculture in the open sea awaits a regime of law there, and effective management as well as more research.

Meanwhile attention is increasingly given to the possibilities of raising more fish and shellfish in coastal waters, where the effort would at least have the protection of national law. Old traditions of shellfish culture are being reexamined,

and one can be confident that scientific bases for further growth will be found. All such activities depend ultimately on what I call "productivity traps": the utilization of natural or artificially modified features of the marine environment to trap biological production originating in a wider area, and by such a biological route that more of the production is embodied in organisms of direct interest to man. In this way we open the immense possibilities of using mangrove swamps and productive estuarine areas, building artificial reefs, breeding even more efficient homing species such as the salmon, enhancing natural production with nutrients or warm water from coastal power stations, controlling predators and competitors, shortening food chains and so on. Progress in such endeavors will require a better predictive ecology than we now have, and also many pilot experiments with corresponding risks of failure as well as chances of success.

The greatest threat to mariculture is perhaps the growing pollution of the sea. This is becoming a real problem for fisheries generally, particularly coastal ones, and mariculture would thrive best in just those regions that are most threatened by pollution, namely the ones near large coastal populations and technological centers. We should not expect, I think, that the ocean would not be used at all as a receptacle for waste—it is in some ways so good for such a purpose: its large volume, its deep holes, the hydrolyzing, corrosive and biologically degrading

properties of seawater and the microbes in it. We should expect, however, that this use will not be an indiscriminate one, that this use of the ocean would be internationally registered, controlled and monitored, and that there would be strict regulation of any dumping of noxious substances (obsolete weapons of chemical and biological warfare, for example), including the injection of such substances by pipelines extending from the coast. There are signs that nations are becoming ready to accept such responsibilities, and to act in concert to overcome the problems. Let us hope that progress in this respect will be faster than it has been in arranging for the management of some fisheries, or in a few decades there may be few coastal fisheries left worth managing.

I have stressed the need for scientific research to ensure the future use of the sea as a source of food. This need seems to me self-evident, but it is undervalued by many persons and organizations concerned with economic development. It is relatively easy to secure a million dollars of international development funds for the worthy purpose of assisting a country to participate in an international fishery or to set up a training school for its fishermen and explore the country's continental shelf for fish or shrimps. It is more difficult to justify a similar or lesser expenditure on the scientific assessment of the new fishery's resources and the investigation of its ocean environment. It is much more difficult to secure even quite limited support for international measures that might ensure the continued profitability of the new fishery for all participants.

Looking back a decade instead of forward, we recall that Lionel A. Walford of the U.S. Fish and Wildlife Service wrote, in a study he made for the Conservation Foundation: "The sea is a mysterious wilderness, full of secrets. It is inhabited only by wild animals and, with the exception of a few special situations, is uncultivated. Most of what we know about it we have had to learn indirectly with mechanical contrivances to probe, feel, sample, fish." There are presumably fewer wild animals now than there were then—at least fewer useful ones—but there seems to be a good chance that by the turn of the century the sea will be less a wilderness and more cultivated. Much remains for us and our children to do to make sure that by then it is not a contaminated wilderness or a battlefield for ever sharper clashes between nations and between the different users of its resources.

IX

Technology and the Ocean

Technology and the Ocean

WILLARD BASCOM

*The materials, machines and techniques that can be employed
in the ocean have advanced greatly during the past decade.
Major developments include superships and deep-sea drilling*

Without technology, meaning knowledge fortified by machinery and tools, men would be ineffective against the sea. During the past decade the technology that can be brought to bear in the oceans has improved enormously and in many ways. The improvements have not only increased knowledge of the oceans but also speeded the flow of commerce while decreasing its cost, brought new mineral provinces within reach and made food from the sea more readily available.

With today's technology it is possible, given a sufficient investment of time and money, to design and build marine hardware that can do almost anything. The problem is to decide whether it is sensible to make a given investment. Industry decides on the basis of whether a proposed technological step will solve a specific problem and improve the firm's competitive position. Government has more latitude: it does not need to show a prompt return on investment, and it can better afford the high risk of developing expensive and exotic devices for which there may be no immediate or clearly defined need. The gains in ocean technology have resulted from the largely independent efforts of both industry and government.

This article will deal broadly with the progress in ocean technology over the past decade, concentrating on developments that seem to be the most important at present. I shall begin by making my own selection of the five most important advances. The main criterion in this selection is that each advance represents an order-of-magnitude improvement: in one way or another it is a tenfold step forward since the beginning of the decade. I have also given weight to the social and economic significance of these developments and to the degree of engineering imagination and perseverance that each one required.

The first development is the supership. Not long ago a "supertanker" carried 35,000 deadweight tons. Now a fleet of ships with nearly 10 times that capacity is coming into being. For these vessels the Panama Canal and the Suez Canal are obsolete. By the same token the ships are making large new demands on the technology that provides the terminal facilities.

Second is the deep-diving submarine. Man can now go to the deep-ocean bottom in an "underwater balloon" submersible such as the *Trieste*, which reached a depth of 36,000 feet in the Mariana Trench 200 miles southwest of Guam. Somewhat more conveniently he can go to a depth of about 6,000 feet in any of several small submarines. This rapidly developing technology still has a long way to go, but it has certainly improved by an order of magnitude in the past decade. Several techniques have

been employed to solve the problem of how to make a submarine hull that is strong enough to resist great pressure and still light enough to return to the surface.

The third development is the ability to drill in deep water. This category includes both the drilling that is done in very deep water for scientific purposes and the use of full-scale drilling equipment on a floating platform to obtain oil from the continental shelf. The first deep-ocean drilling, which was carried out eight years ago by the National Academy of Sciences in water 12,000 feet deep near Guadalupe Island off the west coast of Mexico, improved on four previous records by an order of magnitude: the ship held its position at sea for a month without anchors, drilled in water 20 times deeper than that at earlier marine drilling sites, penetrated 600 feet of the deep-sea floor and lifted weights of 40 tons from the bottom. These records have since been improved on even more. In fact, virtually all floating drilling equipment, including semisubmersible platforms and self-propelled vessels, has been designed and built in the past decade.

Fourth is the ability to navigate precisely. A ship in mid-ocean has rarely known its position within a mile; indeed, five miles is probably closer to the truth, notwithstanding assertions to the contrary. Now a ship 1,000 miles from land can fix its position within .1 mile. If the vessel is within 500 miles of land, the position can be ascertained within .01 mile. The position of a ship within 10 miles of land can be fixed to an accuracy of 10 feet. The techniques for these determinations include orbiting satellites, inertial guidance systems and a number of electronic devices that compare phases of radio waves.

DEEP-SEA DRILLING SHIP *Glomar Challenger* is seen on the opposite page in a photograph made from her drilling tower. The linear arrays on her deck are racks of drilling pipe. The ship is operated by the Scripps Institution of Oceanography under a contract with the National Science Foundation for a deep-sea drilling project that is part of the foundation's National Ocean Sediment Coring Program. The project was planned by the Joint Oceanographic Institutions Deep Earth Sampling (JOIDES) group, which continues to give scientific guidance. Equipped with devices that enable her to hold a precise position in deep water, the ship has drilled 2,500 feet into the sea bottom in water depths to 17,000 feet.

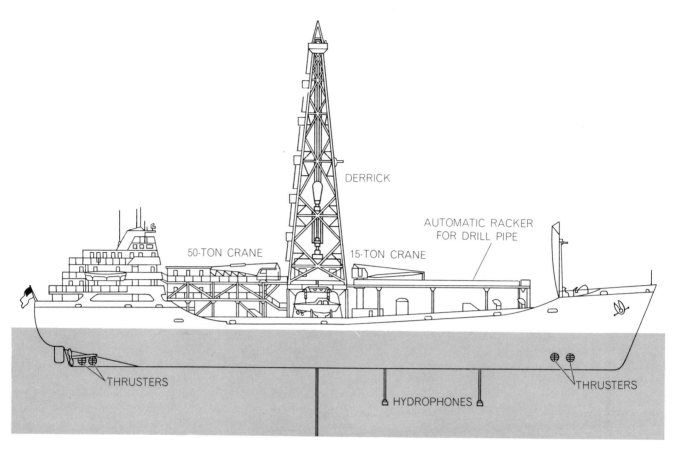

GLOMAR CHALLENGER has a 142-foot derrick as her most conspicuous feature. Her automatic pipe racker can hold 23,000 feet of drill pipe. Positioning equipment includes two tunnel thrusters at the bow and two near the stern to provide for sidewise maneuvers. When the ship is on station (*above*), four hydrophones are extend-

ed under the hull to receive signals from a sonar beacon on the ocean floor. The signals are fed into a computer that controls the thrusters to maintain the ship's position over the drill hole. At the sea bottom (*below*), as much as four miles under the ship, the drill penetrates as much as 2,500 feet of sediment and basement rock.

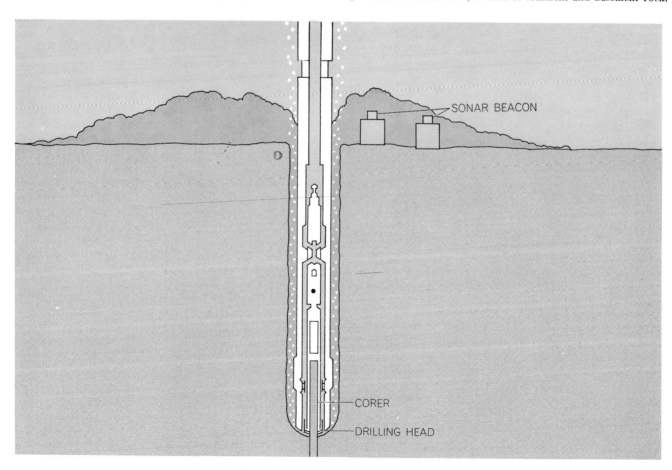

Finally I would cite the ability to examine the ocean bottom in detail from the surface by means of television and side-looking sonar. These techniques, together with their recording devices and the capacity for precise navigation, have made it possible to inspect the sea floor much as land areas have been examined by aerial photography. New television tubes that amplify light by a factor of 30,000 make it possible to eliminate artificial lighting, thereby eliminating also the backscatter of light by small particles in the water.

The supership and the improvement in drilling are mainly industrial developments. The evolution of navigation technology has resulted largely from government efforts. Both industry and government have figured prominently in the development of deep-diving submarines and techniques for examining the bottom with television and sonar.

In considering the application of these and other techniques one might classify them according to who uses them. For example, scientific investigators use research ships and submarines, instruments, buoys, samplers and computers. Industry constantly seeks better methods for mining, fishing, salvage and the production of oil. Waterborne commerce needs better ships, better cargo-handling methods and better port facilities. Exploration becomes more efficient as improved navigational systems, vehicles, geophysical tools and communications equipment become available. Adventure and recreation offer new toys such as air-cushion vehicles and scuba equipment.

The entire area of military technology, which is the most sophisticated of all, must be outside the scope of this article. The best of modern seaborne military technology is done in secrecy, with budgets far in excess of those spent for any of the other areas. Thus we shall not go into such matters as the duel between the submarine builder, who endlessly tries to make submarines go deeper, faster and quieter, and the antisubmarine expert, who tries to detect, identify and destroy the steadily improving submarines.

In any case, the classification of marine technology according to users is somewhat impractical because there is so much overlap. For example, certain kinds of diving and television equipment might be used by all the groups. Therefore I shall discuss marine technology in terms of materials, vehicles, instruments and systems.

What characteristics should a marine material have? It should be light, strong, easy to form and connect, rigid or flexible as desired and inexpensive. The difficulty ocean design engineers have in finding a material that meets most of the requirements for a given task has led them to speak whimsically of an ideal material called "nonobtainium." The problem is that characteristics such as lightness and strength are relative. Nonetheless, engineers and manufacturers recall that not many years ago fiber glass, Dacron and titanium were not obtainable, and so they are optimistic about the development of materials that come ever closer to the qualities of nonobtainium.

In the past decade the steel available for marine purposes has improved substantially under the spur of demands for submarines that can withstand the pressure of great depth, drill pipe (unsupported by the hole wall that pipe in a land well has) that must survive high bending stresses, and great lengths of oceanographic cable that must not twist. For example, a new kind of maraging steel with a high nickel content is tougher, more resistant to notching and less subject to corrosion fatigue than the steel formerly available. The minimum yield strength of conveniently available steel shell plate has risen from 80,000 pounds per square inch to 130,000 pounds per square inch and more for the shells of deep-diving submarines. Steel in wire form now attains a strength of 350,000 pounds per square inch. Steel is becoming more uniform and reliable as the processes of mixing and rolling are subjected to better quality control. Indeed, some metallurgists believe nearly any metal requirement can be met by properly alloyed steel.

Also available for marine purposes are new, high-strength aluminum alloys, such as 5456 (a designation indicating the mix of metals in the alloy), that have a strength of more than 30,000 pounds

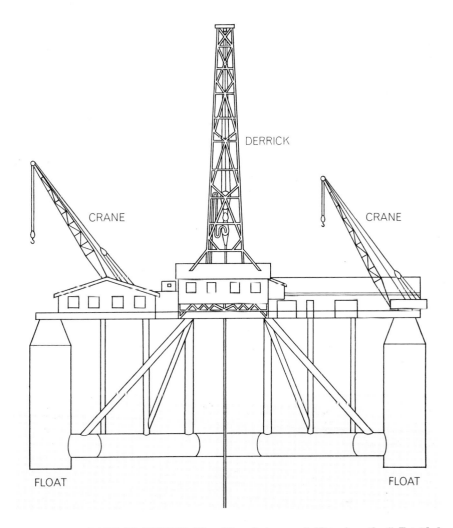

SEMISUBMERSIBLE PLATFORM, *Blue Water 3,* is now drilling for oil off Trinidad. When the platform has been towed to its position, water is drawn into the four corner cylinders to make the structure submerge enough so that wave motions have little effect on it. The platform, which is 220 feet by 198 feet, was designed for work in the open ocean.

per square inch after welding and are resistant to corrosion. They can also be cut with ordinary power saws instead of torches and welded by a technique that is easily taught. With this material small boats, ships up to 2,000 tons and superstructures for much larger ships can be built, as can a number of other structures where lightness and flexibility are important.

Titanium is becoming more readily available. When special properties of lightness, strength (as high as 120,000 pounds per square inch) and good resistance to corrosion are required, its relatively high cost becomes acceptable.

Glass, fiber glass and plastics are the glamorous materials of oceanography. They are virtually free of the problems of corrosion and electrolysis that

SUPERTANKER *UNIVERSE IRELAND* is seen at her loading berth in the Persian Gulf. The vessel, which is 1,135 feet in length, carries 312,000 deadweight tons of oil from the Persian Gulf to Ireland, going around Africa at an average speed of 15 knots.

have afflicted most materials in a marine environment, and they are easily formed into complex shapes. Constant research is improving the strength and versatility of these materials.

Glass is less fragile than most people think and has excellent properties in compression. It is finding increasing favor among the designers of small submarines, who want a glass-bubble pressure hull that is also a superwindow. Glass microspheres, which do the same thing as a submarine hull but on a microscopic scale, are packaged in blocks of epoxy and used to furnish incompressible flotation at depths of as much as 20,000 feet. The best such material to withstand the pressure at that depth so far weighs about 40 pounds per cubic foot; in seawater at 64 pounds per cubic foot the material therefore has a net buoyancy of 24 pounds per cubic foot.

The many remarkable characteristics of fiber glass are widely known. Its outstanding virtue as a marine material is that it enables precisely shaped hulls with complex lines to be reproduced easily. The result has been a revolution in the construction of small craft over the past decade. Fiber-glass hulls, which are light and strong without a rib structure, are a major contribution to marine technology and a boon to the small-boat owners, whose maintenance problems are reduced accordingly.

Among the plastics polyvinyl chloride has found use in marine pipelines subject to severe internal corrosion. It is light, inexpensive and easily joined. Nylon and polypropylene for cordage and fishing nets and Dacron for sails are appreciated by all sailors because the materials are light and elastic and do not rot. Ship-bottom paints, designed to reduce fouling by marine organisms, have been greatly improved. Inorganic zinc underpaints promise to decrease substantially the pitting of hulls and decks, which should increase the life of ships and the time between dry-dockings.

A remarkable collection of marine vehicles and equipment has made its appearance in the past 10 years. Ships now exist that can go up, down and sideways and can flip. They skim, fly and dive. Some of them are amphibious and some go through ice, over ice or under it.

This versatility is important; a ship cannot be efficient unless it has been designed to do exactly what the user wants. Widely varying requirements mean very different sea vehicles. A distinct place on the spectrum is occupied by the superships I mentioned earlier. They are

ALUMINAUT, a mobile submersible capable of carrying two crew and four passengers to depths of 15,000 feet and of probing the bottom or moving heavy objects with manipulator arms attached to the hull, is photographed during a dive. The craft is 51 feet in length.

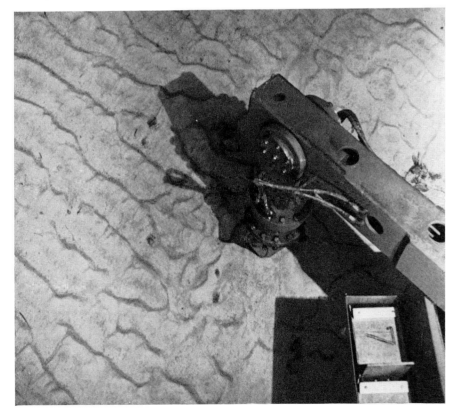

MANIPULATOR ARM of *Aluminaut* explores bottom off Bimini at a depth of nearly 1,800 feet. Numbered sample boxes are nearby. Thin layer of sand is rippled by a current moving it over a rock base; the dark areas are debris that are caught in filamentous organisms attached to rock. Photograph was made by A. Conrad Neumann of the University of Miami.

bigger than anyone dreamed of only a few years ago; in fact, they are almost the largest man-made structures. The largest vessel now in service is the *Universe Ireland,* a tanker with a capacity of 312,000 deadweight tons. The ship is 1,135 feet long and delivers 37,400 shaft horsepower. It plies between the Persian Gulf and Ireland, going around Africa at 15 knots and pushing a 12-foot breaking wave ahead of it. Even the enormous vessels of the *Universe Ireland* class will soon be surpassed in size by ships being built in Japan and West Germany. They will be so large they will not be able to dry-dock in any yard except where they were built, and they will not be able to enter any ordinary harbor because they will draw up to 80 feet of water.

A variation in the tanker field is the conversion of the comparatively small (114,000 deadweight-ton capacity) *Manhattan* to a supericebreaker. The purpose is to move the petroleum from the large new oil fields on the northern slope of Alaska to more moderate climates. A fleet of such ships may be able to keep open a northwest passage from the U.S. East Coast to Alaska. From ships of the

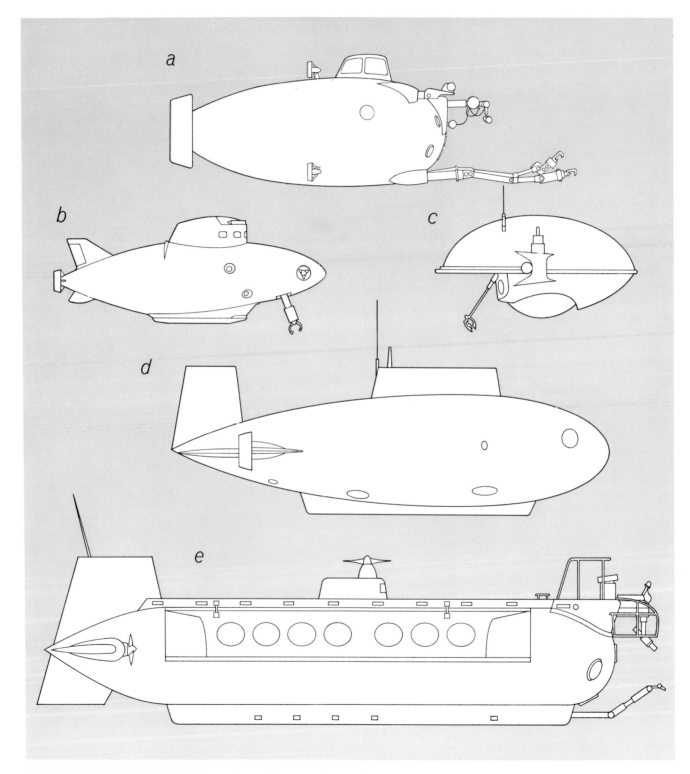

MANNED RESEARCH SUBMARINES are designed for deep diving. They include (*a*) *Beaver IV,* which can dive to 2,000 feet; (*b*) *Star III,* to 2,000 feet; (*c*) *Deepstar IV,* to 4,000 feet; (*d*) *Deep* *Quest,* to 8,000 feet, and (*e*) *Aluminaut,* which is designed to go to 15,000 feet with a staff of six. Vessels are drawn to scale. *Aluminaut* is made primarily of aluminum; the others are steel craft.

Manhattan class it is only a small step conceptually to a ship five times larger that could cross the Arctic Ocean at will, treating the ice, which averages eight feet in thickness, as an annoying scum.

The ships that go up include both the ground-effect machine, which can rise a few feet above the surface of the sea on a cushion of air, and the hydrofoil, which has a hull that flies above the surface at high speed with the support of small, precisely shaped underwater foils. The newest versions of these "flying boats" represent substantial technical achievements, and yet neither vehicle seems likely to become a very important factor in marine affairs because each has basic problems, such as the danger to the hydrofoil of hitting heavy flotsam and the inability of the ground-effect machine to carry large loads or to operate in high waves. The ground-effect machine does have a potential, not much exploited as yet, stemming from its ability to run up a beach and cross mud flats, ice and smooth land surfaces.

The ships that go down are of course

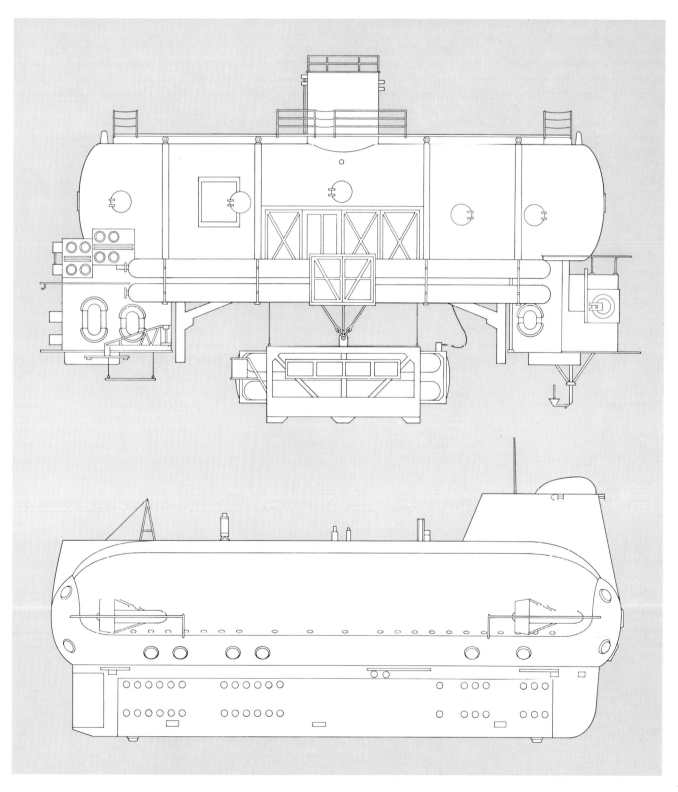

UNDERWATER LABORATORIES include the Navy's *Sealab III* (*top*) and the Grumman-Piccard submersible *Ben Franklin* (*bottom*). *Sealab* is designed to operate on the sea bottom, where it will provide living quarters for divers who will venture forth periodically in heated diving suits to explore the bottom. The first mission of *Ben Franklin* was a submerged drift up the Gulf Stream.

submarines. Nuclear power in military submarines dates back further than the decade under discussion, but large advances in nuclear propulsion have been made during the decade. The circumnavigation of the earth without surfacing and the trip under ice to the North Pole were both made possible by nuclear power and highly developed life-support systems for keeping the crews alive and well on the long missions.

Quite a number of small, deep-diving submarines are in existence. Of them the *Aluminaut*, designed to go to 15,000 feet while carrying six people, has accomplished the most. (Because of the problem of obtaining life insurance for its crew its deepest dive has been about 6,000 feet.) Among the many other small submarines are the ones of the *Alvin* class, which can dive to 6,000 feet; *Deep Quest*, to 8,000 feet; *Deepstar IV*, to 4,000 feet; *Beaver IV* and *Star III*, to 2,000 feet, and *Deep Diver*, to 1,000 feet. There is therefore a considerable choice of vehicles, instruments and supporting facilities. The problem is that there are few customers with the inclination to employ these vehicles at $1,000 or more per hour of diving.

The ships that move sideways are those with trainable propellers or vertical-axis propellers or tunnel thrusters. (A tunnel thruster enables a pilot to move the ship's bow sideways.) Vessels so equipped have found use in self-docking situations and in such waterways as the St. Lawrence Seaway. Dynamic positioning, which means holding position without anchors, is possible with ships that have precise local-navigation systems and central control of several maneuvering propellers.

The ship that flips is *FLIP*, operated by the Scripps Institution of Oceanography. It has two positions of stability. While it is under tow it lies on the surface and looks like a barge made from a big piece of pipe. On station it ballasts itself so as to float on end, much like a big, habitable buoy. In this position *FLIP*, because of its size, is detuned from the motion of the sea surface: it does not move vertically under the influence of ordinary waves and swell. As a result it is an excellent platform for making underwater sound measurements.

Among instruments and tools the now venerable sonar, the sound-ranging device, still figures prominently. It has been improved substantially. Frequencies have risen steadily, making it possible to narrow the beam width to searchlight dimensions, with the result that the distance to (or depth of) discrete areas of the ocean bottom can be measured more accurately. Sonars employing the Doppler effect, which is the change of pitch of a sound resulting from relative motion between the source and the observer, make possible the direct measurement of a ship's speed over the bottom—a measurement that is essential to the high-quality navigation required for such purposes as determining gravity at sea by means of a shipboard gravity me-

ter. Frequency-scanning sonars are now available that better match the signal with the reflector.

Hydrophone arrays, sometimes a mile long, make it possible to use the low-frequency sound created by a series of gas explosions to examine the rocks under the sea bottom in great detail. The result is a continuous picture of a vertical geologic section. Such continuous-reflection seismic profiles have revealed folds and faults in sub-bottom rocks to depths of as much as 15,000 feet and have found many new undersea oil deposits.

Satellites are valuable ocean instruments. They are the essential elements in the system that makes it possible to determine a ship's position accurately wherever it may be. Other satellites transmit photographs of weather patterns, cloud cover and the state of the sea. By combining the picture with other weather data, meteorologists can produce accurate charts with reliable and up-to-date information. The information is useful in routing ships and forecasting waves.

Buoys moored in the deep ocean hold instruments for measuring, recording and transmitting sea and weather conditions. A number of buoys are already in use, producing an abundance of hitherto unavailable information at minimal expense. It seems likely that hundreds of additional buoys will be put to work in the next few years.

Shipboard computers are becoming an accepted convenience. Such a computer plots the ship's position continuously and matches it with accumulating data of other kinds so that investigators aboard the ship have an information system describing the pulse of the sea below them.

Occasionally a single device can revolutionize an industry. Such a device is the Puretic power block, which han-

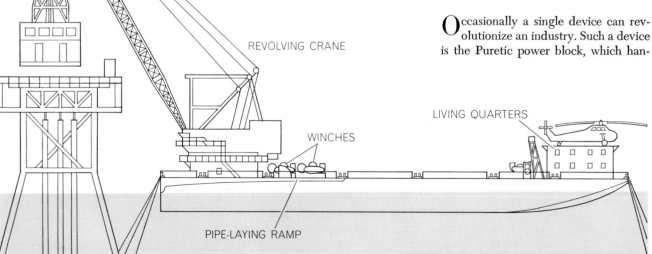

REVOLVING CRANE

WINCHES

LIVING QUARTERS

PIPE-LAYING RAMP

CONSTRUCTION BARGE, the *William Denny,* is about to be put in ocean operation by Raymond International Inc. It is 350 feet long and 25 feet deep and has a 100-foot beam. Its revolving crane, which has a 250-foot boom, can lift 500 tons at a 70-foot radius and 100 tons at a 215-foot radius. The craft can lift 750 tons over the stern. It can build structures, drive piles and lay pipelines.

dles fishing nets. It is, like many good inventions, basically simple: it is a wide-mouthed, rubber-lined pulley driven by a small hydraulic motor. During the past decade it has been adopted by many fishing fleets and now accounts for some 40 percent of the world's catch. With the block it is possible to handle much larger nets with fewer men. One result is that the tuna industry has shifted almost entirely from line fishing to net fishing.

Another trend in fishing has been to put fish-processing equipment on boats.

The equipment includes automatic filleting machines, quick-freeze boxes and even packaging machines so that a finished frozen product can be delivered at dockside. Scallops, for example, can now be shucked and eviscerated on shipboard, so that the scalloper can remain at sea for a week at a time and return with a cargo of ready-to-eat scallops.

Barge-mounted cranes capable of lifting 600-ton loads as much as 200 feet above the water are now available along many coasts. The result is a change in

construction techniques. For example, a bridge can be built in large sections, which are then hoisted into place by the crane.

Shipyards are using elevators called Syncrolifts to lift and launch ships weighing as much as 6,000 tons. The machines are replacing dry docks and marine railways. The Syncrolift is simply a big platform that can be lowered below keel depth. A ship is then floated in, and a dozen or more synchronized winches hoist it up to the level of a transfer rail-

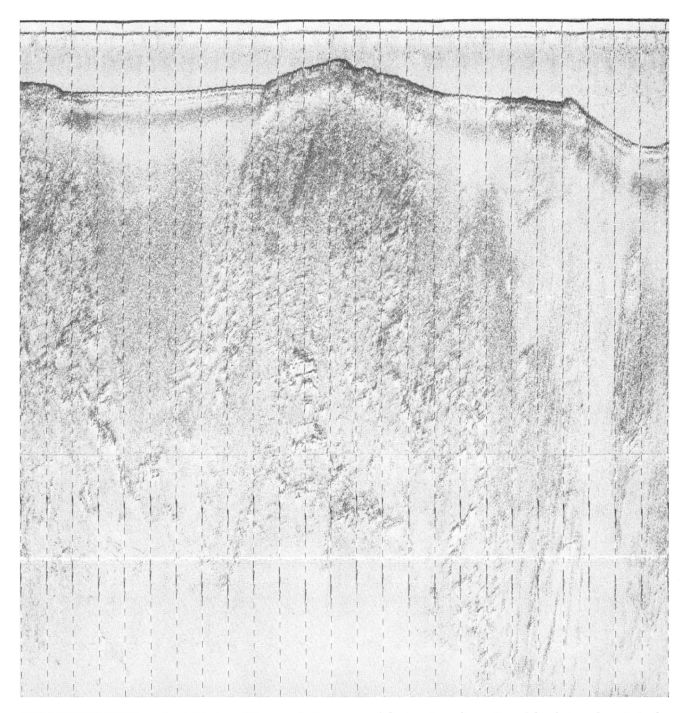

SIDE-LOOKING SONAR produced this view of the ocean bottom on the continental shelf northeast of Boston. From right to left the record covers a distance of about two kilometers along the ship's track. Broken lines show one-minute intervals. Irregular line near top is a profile view of the sea bottom as it appeared at the instru-ment's horizon. Irregular portions of the photograph are bedrock; darker flat areas are sand waves and gravel; lighter flat areas are smooth sand. Bottom was 60 to 140 meters below the ship. Record was made by John E. Sanders of Barnard College and K. O. Emery and Elazar Uchupi of Woods Hole Oceanographic Institution.

way, which moves it to a position in the yard. In this way the yard can work on several ships simultaneously.

The first undersea dredge has just made its appearance. The machine moves along the bottom on crawler tracks in depths of as much as 200 feet. Hence it is not affected by the wave action that makes life on floating dredges hard. The machine was designed to replace eroding beaches with sand from offshore: the dredge has a 700-horse-power pump that moves the sand slurry a mile to shore.

It is fashionable now to speak of the "systems approach," which is a way of expressing the obvious idea that all the elements in the solution of a problem should fit together and be headed toward the same goal. All the ships and instruments I have described are employed as parts of systems. There are, however, several integrated combinations of technology that are best described under the heading of systems. They include containerized cargo-handling, desalination of seawater, deep-ocean drilling and deep diving.

Containerization has become a magic word on the waterfront. The basic idea is that a shipper can move his goods from his inland manufacturing point to an inland customer overseas in a private container. A container moves by train or truck to a marshaling yard on the waterfront. There it is picked up by a straddle truck and moved within reach of a gantry crane, which sets it in slots on a container ship. The contents are safe from pilferage, weather and damage. A harbor facility, dealing with containers of standardized size, can semiautomatically unload and reload a large cargo ship in less than 24 hours. Labor cost is lowered; the ship spends more time at sea and less alongside a dock, and the freight moves faster and more cheaply than on a break-bulk cargo ship [see "Cargo-handling," by Roger H. Gilman; SCIENTIFIC AMERICAN, October, 1968].

Methods for desalting water have been improved substantially. The world-wide use of desalted water from the sea is now almost 100 million gallons per day. Most of the water is obtained by various distillation processes; the average cost is estimated to be about 75 cents per 1,000 gallons. Other means of desalination, such as vacuum freezing and reverse osmosis, are being developed. Major nuclear plants that would produce both fresh water and electricity are under study. Most of the desalted water now obtained or in prospect is for house-

hold and industrial purposes. The day of cheap irrigation water in large quantities is still far away.

Offshore drilling from floating platforms is less than a decade old and has evolved rapidly. The self-propelled drilling ship and the semisubmersible platform, both of which drill while anchored, represent the two ends of the spectrum. The ship emphasizes speed of movement to the drilling site; the platform provides more steadiness and room for working. A semisubmersible platform is towed to its drilling site, where it takes on enough water ballast to submerge its lower portions. In that position it floats on large cylindrical columns. The arrangement is such that the platform is little affected by waves or other motions of the sea.

The unanchored deep-ocean drilling system, which consists of a drilling rig in a ship hull, has so far been used only for scientific work. It has improved substantially the ability of geologists and other investigators to explore the strata under the deep ocean. The technology dates from 1961 and includes dynamic positioning, the control of stress in a long and unsupported drill pipe, placement of conductor pipe (leading the drill through the soft sea bottom to bedrock) in deep water and the use of a seawater turbodrill to drill hard rock in more than 12,000 feet of water.

Later developments have led to the system employed on the *Glomar Challenger*, which is operated by the Scripps Institution of Oceanography in a National Science Foundation program involving the coring of deep-ocean sediments in water depths of up to 20,000 feet [*see illustration on page 110*]. The developments include acoustical position-sensing equipment and automatic control of the propulsion units, so that dynamic positioning is much more reliable. The ship has successfully drilled several dozen holes in water depths to 17,000 feet, penetrating as much as 2,500 feet of the sea bottom. The cores thus obtained have yielded much valuable information. Moreover, the discovery of hydrocarbons on Sigsbee Knolls deep in the Gulf of Mexico has done much to modify geological thinking about the possibility of oil in deep water.

Offshore oil production is moving steadily into deeper and rougher water and more remote areas. If it is to be profitable, several producing wells must be established in each cluster and the capital cost should not exceed the present cost of producing oil in 200 feet of

water. Probably it is possible to build stationary platforms that would resemble existing ones for depths of up to 600 feet. The cost would be high, however, particularly for a system that involved completing the well atop the platform

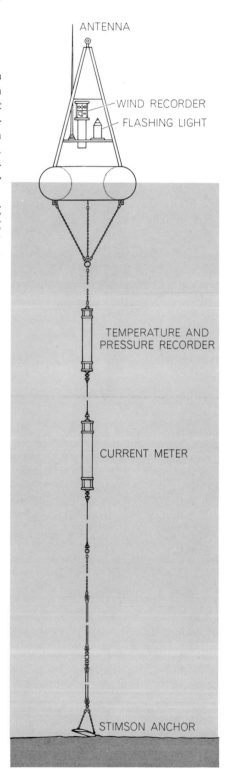

BIG RESEARCH BUOY employed by the Woods Hole Oceanographic Institution gathers and transmits data from the surface to the sea floor. At the surface it records wind speed and direction; below the surface it measures temperature, pressure and current.

(installing the pipes and valves and related equipment needed to put the well into production after drilling has reached oil). The current trend is toward the use of floating drilling platforms such as the semisubmersible ones, with completion of the well being made on the sea floor. A system of this kind would include remotely controlled valves and flow lines to central collecting points. In depths of 1,000 feet or more submarine work chambers analogous to pressure-resistant elevators will lower workmen to the bottom; while they remain inside at normal surface pressure they will be able to remove and replace heavy components, make flow-line and electrical connections and inspect the machinery.

HOISTING DEVICE called the Syncrolift allows the Canadian submarine *Ojibwa* to be lifted out of the water (*above*) and pulled ashore on rails (*below*) for repair in a dockyard at Halifax, Nova Scotia. The platform is lowered under the keel of a vessel, the ship is floated in and the platform is raised by the array of winches visible in the photograph. The device has a capacity of 6,000 tons.

Deep diving is receiving increasing attention in ocean technology. Men go into increasingly deeper water by means of systems that grow ever more complicated, involving a variety of chambers, hoists, gases and instruments. There are two competing methods: the bounce dive and the saturation dive. In a bounce dive the diver goes from atmospheric pressure to the required depth in a chamber, breathing gaseous mixtures that change in accordance with depth and physiological requirements. He works for a few minutes (perhaps 10) and then returns to the surface in a fully pressurized chamber for slow decompression on the deck of the mother ship. The saturation-dive system makes possible multiple dives. In it the diver's body is saturated with inert gases while he lives in a pressure chamber on shipboard. When it is time to dive, he moves into a similarly pressurized capsule that is lowered to the bottom. Since his body is already prepared for the pressure, he can immediately go to work. He can work much longer than the bounce diver before he returns to the capsule and thence to the chamber on deck. Since he lives on the surface but at the pressure of the bottom, the procedure can be repeated for many days. Then the diver takes a slow decompression to atmospheric pressure. Divers using each of these systems have reached 1,000 feet.

Another scheme has divers living on the bottom in shallow water at ambient pressures in undersea chambers. Examples are the experiments that have been carried out in such chamber systems as the U.S. Navy's *Sealab II*, the University of Miami's *Tektite* and the French *Conshelf*.

Doubtless oceanographers can point to elements of ocean technology I have overlooked. The developments have been too rapid and profuse for one man to be familiar with them all. Sometimes one feels that the first question to be asked on hearing about a new oceanographic device is: "Is it obsolete yet?" The answer should be: "We're working on that problem and it soon will be."

DIVING GEOLOGISTS of the Shell Oil Company probe the ocean floor at a depth of about 20 feet on the Bahama Banks. The pipe and hose slanting across the center are parts of an air-lift apparatus that they are using to obtain information helpful in the search for oil.

X

The Ocean and Man

The Ocean and Man

WARREN S. WOOSTER

The increase of human activity in the sea presents deep problems of relations among nations. Who owns the resources of the sea, and how is the worldwide exploration of the sea to be organized?

The quickening of human activity in the oceans that has been chronicled in the preceding articles brings the problem of international cooperation in ocean study and management increasingly to the fore. Most of the world is ocean, and most of the ocean lies beyond the limits of national jurisdiction and is subject to no specific ownership. How, then, are the steadily more complex techniques for studying the ocean to be organized, financed and applied? How are the resources of the sea to be apportioned? Who is to regulate human activity in the sea so that it brings maximum benefits to mankind and at the same time does not result in harmful effects such as pollution?

The problem has a number of facets. One is the vastness of the area in question. The ocean waters cover four-fifths of the Southern Hemisphere and more than three-fifths of the Northern Hemisphere. The world ocean contains about 1,350 million cubic kilometers of water at an average depth of almost four kilometers.

Another consideration arises from the unity of the ocean. The waters and their contents mingle freely. The processes operating in the waters are of large scale and are driven by forces of planetary dimension. Life in the ocean is affected by these processes, so that the type, number and distribution of organisms may be controlled by events occurring in distant places. Because of this immense unity, investigation of the world ocean is inherently an international affair, requiring cooperation ranging from the simplest exchange of information to the most complex integration of research programs.

Man lives on continental islands embedded in the vast surrounding sea, and many of his activities involve it or are affected by it. To him it is a means of transport and a font of resources. It affects him also by being a reservoir of heat, so that weather and climate across the continents are determined to a large extent by events at the ocean surface.

Conversely, man now has the ability to affect the ocean, sometimes deliberately and sometimes inadvertently and often far from the site of the intervention. A film of oil coats the animals and beaches of southern California, pesticides applied on the African continent appear in the Bay of Bengal and a healthy, succulent oyster becomes a rarity. More subtle forms of intervention are being practiced. For example, completion of the Aswan Dam has almost halted the annual release of water from the Nile into the eastern Mediterranean. The nutrient elements the river water supplied every year gave rise to a proliferation of fish that supported a commercial fishery. Another effect of the flow was an annual decrease in the surface salinity of the Mediterranean for several hundred miles north of the river. Now these waters are no longer enriched, and the increased salinity and density of the surface water may affect mixing processes along much of the eastern shore of the Mediterranean in a way that is difficult to predict.

Another form of intervention is the linking of separate bodies of water by man-made straits. What oceanographic consequences might a sea-level canal across the Isthmus of Panama have if current proposals to build one are carried out? Evidence provided by the link between the Red Sea and the eastern Mediterranean through the Suez Canal is suggestive. During the first decades after the canal was opened the high salinity of the Bitter Lakes barred the exchange of animals between the two seas. As these lakes have gradually freshened by being connected with the eastern Mediterranean through the canal the barrier has been losing effectiveness, and Red Sea organisms are slowly invading the Mediterranean.

Most of the ocean research now being done is conducted by investigators in a small number of affluent countries. The major participants are Canada, France, Germany, Japan, the United Kingdom, the U.S. and the U.S.S.R. Many more countries use the ocean, particularly for fishing, and the technical capability of the developing nations for exploiting ocean resources is increasing. (Peru, for example, has in recent years operated the world's largest fishery.) The ability of such nations to conduct research has not advanced so rapidly, which is regrettable because of the importance to a developing country of participating in ocean research off its coasts. The coastal state has the most direct and immediate need to know the natural resources available to it. In the case of living resources it needs to know the relation between the ocean environment and the abundance, distribution and availability of the organisms. When a nation participates in ocean research, it can develop a corps of investigators who, through their own work and their interaction with workers from other nations, can interpret data on marine resources and the ocean environment and so contribute to the formulation by the country of a rational policy for the management of ocean resources.

It is plain enough that nations ought to cooperate in investigating the ocean. What kinds of international action are most desirable, and how can they be most effectively arranged?

The most basic form of scientific cooperation is the exchange of data and other information. Until about 20 years ago the community of oceanographers

123

SPREAD OF OIL over the Santa Barbara Channel from the offshore well that began leaking in January 1969 is shown in the photograph on the opposite page. The photograph was made during peak flow in February, when the amount of oil escaping was estimated at several thousand barrels a day.

was so small that most of the members knew one another and could exchange information on a personal basis. Now the number of oceanographers is much larger, so that personal evaluation of reported work is often impossible. Moreover, the flow of data has increased enormous-

ly. For example, determination of the vertical distribution of temperature and salinity in the upper kilometer of the ocean is a common requirement. Formerly a measurement might be made with 20 sampling devices; the basic observation would require about an hour, and about two more hours would be needed to determine and plot the 60 corrected values (temperature, salinity and pressure at each of 20 depths) the apparatus had obtained. The data rate was 20 values per hour. Now observations are often made with *in situ* devices capable of giving values of temperature, salinity

and pressure at one-meter intervals. The total observation may require 45 minutes; by then the oceanographer has available, already plotted on a strip chart, some 3,000 values. The data rate has become 4,000 values per hour—higher than the previous rate by a factor of 200.

Related to the increase of oceanographic activity is the problem of making data comparable. Many investigations require the pooling of data from a number of sources. The synthesis is particularly difficult when different methods and standards have been used. In

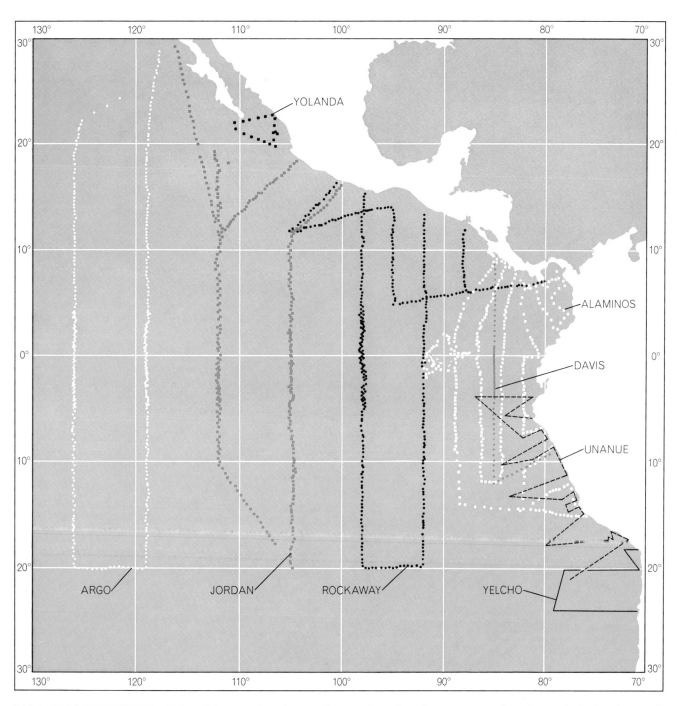

EASTROPAC EXPEDITION, which took its name from its area of operations in the eastern tropical Pacific, was an international surveying and sampling venture that involved eight ships from four nations. One of seven two-month cruises made during the expedition is mapped; dots show where each named ship took samples. Expedition was carried out in 1967 by U.S., Mexico, Chile and Peru.

recent years a considerable effort has been made, by experiments in intercomparison and by the development of methods of reference, to improve comparability.

Increased oceanographic activity has led to the broadening and improvement of the international system of data exchange. Such a system had existed on a regional basis for many years in northern Europe: the Hydrographic Service of the International Council for the Exploration of the Sea had collected and published data from its members since 1902. By the 1950's, however, most data

were coming from regions other than the North Atlantic and a more general system of exchange was required.

The International Geophysical Year, conducted during 1957 and 1958 by the International Union of Geodesy and Geophysics, provided an opportunity to establish a series of world data centers in a number of fields of geophysics. Two oceanographic data centers, established in Washington and Moscow, are still in operation. By now their catalogues list many thousands of useful observations, although the time has come, if the centers are to keep abreast of requirements, when the facilities should be trans-

formed from archives to modern computer-based operations.

The international exchanges during the International Geophysical Year were made on a nongovernmental basis. Since 1961 the desirability of governmental commitments to exchange data has been recognized. Governments now make such commitments through the Intergovernmental Oceanographic Commission, an adjunct of the United Nations Educational, Scientific and Cultural Organization.

With the postwar expansion of oceanographic facilities it became possible to look beyond local waters and consid-

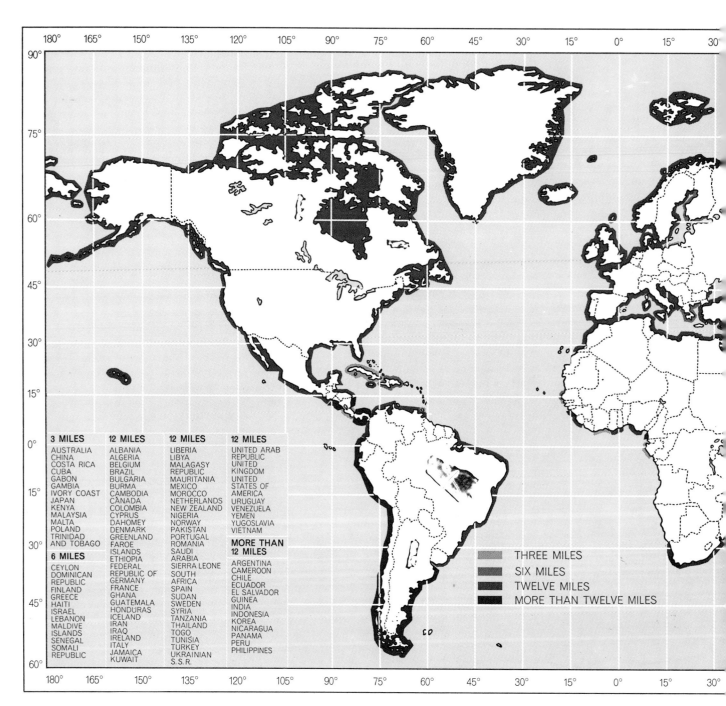

FISHING JURISDICTION claimed by various nations ranges from three miles to 200 miles. The claims shown are based on information published by the American Assembly last year. Additional rights have been claimed by Cambodia, Ceylon, Ghana, Korea, Nicer extending investigations over much larger portions of the ocean. The first manifestation of the trend was a series of single-ship circumnavigations, including those of the Swedish *Albatross,* the Danish *Galathea* and the British *Challenger.* Similar expeditions continue to be mounted, although one would think they would be difficult to justify in the absence of some newly recognized phenomenon or new observational capability that warranted a global exploration.

An important recent trend has been toward more comprehensive investigations made cooperatively by ships from a number of laboratories. The ships may make reasonably simultaneous observations over large areas of the ocean. A case in point is the EASTROPAC Expedition, which derived its name from its area of operation, the eastern tropical Pacific. During one two-month period of this expedition eight ships from the U.S., Mexico, Peru and Chile took readings at some 1,700 stations, sampling an area about a fourth as large as the entire Atlantic Ocean. Such investigations have ranged from the loosely coordinated International Indian Ocean Expedition to the more synchronized International Cooperative Investigations of the Tropical Atlantic.

The requirement for such multiship investigations arises in the study of processes of very large dimensions. When the rates of these processes are comparable with the time it takes to observe them, an adequate description demands simultaneous observations over the entire region affected by the process. It is unlikely that a single laboratory or even a single nation commands the necessary observational resources. Even when simultaneous observations are not required, because the rates of processes are slow (as in deep water or on the ocean floor), the need to obtain the desired spatial resolution calls for a large number of observations. A case in point would be an attempt to describe the present form of the sea floor. In such undertakings a collective effort makes possible the completion of the description in a reasonable period of time.

In the mounting of such efforts it is important to take into account the enormous range of oceanic phenomena—in time from seconds to millenniums and in space from centimeters to thousands of kilometers. One year may differ dramatically from another. For example, the International Geophysical Year, which included much oceanographic work, took place during a period of unusual solar activity (indeed, the timing of the program was chosen for that reason), and it is not surprising that the period turned out to be aberrant in the ocean and the atmosphere. Much of the Pacific Ocean in particular was highly anomalous in behavior, with strong warming in the eastern North Pacific and a well-developed El Niño (the appearance of a warm surface layer over the cold Peru Current, usually with far-reaching effects on marine life and the weather of coastal regions) off the coast of South America. Thus if one were to draw conclusions about the oceanography of the eastern Pacific solely from the observations made during 1957 and 1958, the conclusions could be highly misleading.

The mounting of multiship expeditions requires a much higher level of cooperation than the exchange of information. As recently as 10 years ago most cooperative studies of the ocean were organized directly by the investigators concerned; governments had the passive role of providing funds. It became evident, however, that the financial requirements were growing and that international cooperation might be more effective if formal commitments were made by the participating governments. Such commitments are now made through the Intergovernmental Oceano-

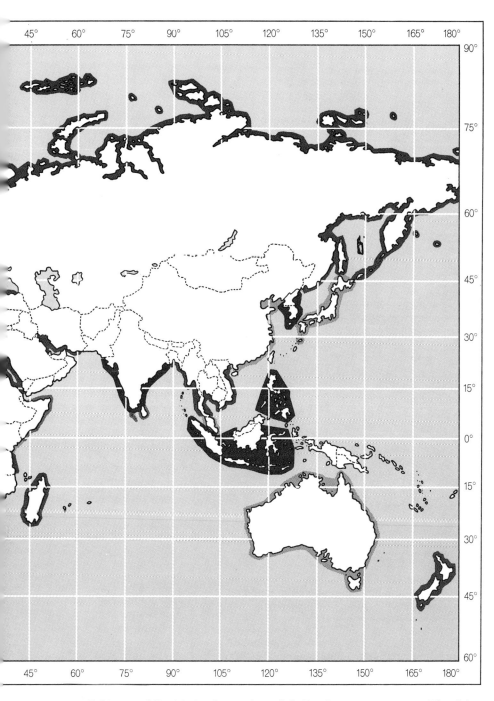

aragua, Pakistan and Tunisia for the continental shelf and superjacent waters. The claims indicate the difficulties involved in obtaining international agreement on use of the ocean.

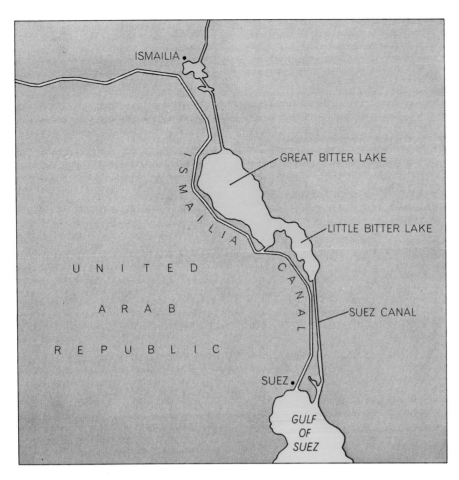

SUEZ REGION has been affected by a decline of salinity of the Bitter Lakes in the 100 years since the opening of the Suez Canal. The high salinity of the lakes originally prevented the exchange of animals between the Red Sea and the eastern Mediterranean through the canal, but as the lakes have freshened, the barrier has gradually lost its effectiveness.

graphic Commission, an organization created for that purpose in 1960. This commission has already acquired considerable experience in a number of large-scale cooperative investigations. It seems likely to play a central role in organizing and coordinating the International Decade of Ocean Exploration that was proposed by President Johnson in 1968 to be conducted during the 1970's.

Another field that depends on international cooperation is the provision of global services. Many of the services

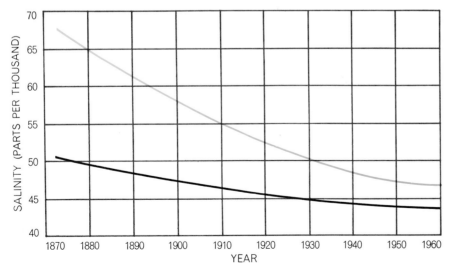

DECLINE OF SALINITY in Great Bitter Lake resulting from infusion of fresher waters by way of the Suez Canal is charted for the lake bottom (color) and for the surface (black).

required by oceanographers are extensions of those provided for a number of years to other kinds of mariners. An example is the bathymetric chart, or depth chart, prepared for coastal waters by the various national hydrographic offices coordinated by the International Hydrographic Organization in Monaco. Traditionally mariners have been interested only in the topography of coastal regions and other places where they might run aground. Now the interests of ocean scientists, fishermen, oil companies and governments require detailed knowledge of the entire continental margin. Soon charts of the deep-sea floor will be needed for the same broad spectrum of users.

The need for a precise, reliable and broadly available global system of navigation is becoming urgent. Satellite systems and other techniques now give promise of precise positioning anywhere in the ocean at any time. This capability is as necessary for the development of sea-floor mineral resources as it is for research.

The needs of weather forecasting have given rise to a network of ships and island stations that make observations at the sea surface and transmit them to central stations for use in weather analyses. Even though the coverage is inadequate over most of the ocean, it is possible to get a crude picture of conditions on a given day, particularly in the Northern Hemisphere. Gaps in the observational coverage will be filled during the next decade by satellites and patterns of fixed and drifting buoys, measuring near-surface conditions in both the ocean and the atmosphere and transmitting their data via satellite to central stations. The instrumentation of the ocean in this fashion is being considered for the World Weather Watch of the World Meteorological Organization (a UN agency) and for its oceanographic counterpart, the Integrated Global Ocean Station System of the Intergovernmental Oceanographic Commission. Both operations at sea and the investigation of time-dependent oceanic phenomena will benefit from the improved descriptions and forecasts made possible by these monitoring systems.

So far I have confined my discussion largely to the scientific aspects of international cooperation in the ocean. The nonscientific problems—be they political, legal, organizational, social or economic—are far more complex. They deserve a more penetrating analysis than is possible here, but a few examples will illustrate their nature.

An important legal and political problem with a direct impact on ocean science is that of the freedom of research. Oceanic features and processes are little affected by boundary lines drawn on charts. Investigations must be made on the basis of phenomena rather than political boundaries.

Up to the present there have been no significant restrictions on research on the high seas. On the continental margins, on the other hand, the 1958 Geneva Convention on the Continental Shelf states that "the consent of the coastal State shall be obtained in respect of any research concerning the continental shelf and undertaken there." The convention defines the shelf as "adjacent to the coast but outside the area of the territorial sea" and extending "to a depth of 200 meters or, beyond that limit, to where the depth of the superjacent waters admits of the exploitation of the natural resources of the said area." The open-ended nature of this definition leaves in doubt how widely the restriction of obtaining consent will be applied.

A further difficulty arises from the convention's statement that "the coastal State exercises over the continental shelf sovereign rights for the purpose of exploring it and exploiting its resources." Presumably exploration in this context means the detailed pre-exploitation survey that might better be called prospecting. True exploration, however, is a fundamental element of oceanic research, and scientific exploration must not be excluded from the freedom of research.

As coastal states contemplate the resource potential of their shelves and nearshore waters they become more reluctant to permit foreign scientists to work there. Unless the research is done, however, neither the resources nor the associated environmental factors are likely to be revealed. Hence it would appear generally advantageous for permission to be granted under the conditions that all findings are made freely available and that scientists of the coastal state can participate fully in the research.

Agreement on principles and workable rules for the rational use of the ocean and its resources will require international cooperation of the highest degree. Considerable interest in this problem has already been shown by the UN. In 1967 Malta proposed a treaty that would vest ownership of the mineral resources of the sea beyond national jurisdiction in an international regime and would assign the profits from the exploitation of resources to the development of poor nations. The General

Assembly responded by establishing an *ad hoc* committee to study the peaceful uses of the ocean floor. A year later the Assembly established a permanent committee of 42 nations to continue the work. The Assembly also initiated consideration of the possible harmful effects that might arise from exploitation of seabed resources and welcomed the concept of an International Decade of Ocean Exploration.

It must be recognized that the potential resources of the deep-sea bed cannot be exploited economically today and that for the foreseeable future only a few countries will have the technical capability even for prospecting and pilot exploitation. There remains, however, a strong feeling among the disadvantaged nations that the resources of the deep-sea bed should ultimately benefit those with the greatest needs. These feelings account for the many efforts that have been made in recent years to establish an international regime over this vast territory, which has been estimated to represent five-sevenths of the earth's area. For such a regime to be effective it must stimulate rather than inhibit the development of the resources, provide for their rational management and conservation and facilitate an equitable distribution of the benefits received from them.

Attempts to manage international fisheries have already shown some of the difficulties of obtaining international agreement on the oceans. More than 20

GIANT BUOY, part of a network of buoys involved in the North Pacific Experiment sponsored by the Navy's Office of Naval Research, is towed to its station 1,000 miles north of Hawaii by the Coast Guard cutter *Yocona.* The buoy gathers and transmits oceanographic and meteorological data on surface winds, barometric pressure, waves, surface current, and temperature and salinity, pressure and temperature at various depths. The radial array at top of buoy and the cone of wires descending therefrom form the buoy's antenna system.

international fishery conventions are in effect. Even the most successful of them faces problems in obtaining and evaluating the scientific information required for establishing effective management procedures and in receiving the full cooperation of all affected nations in implementing the procedures. Significant improvement in the use of the ocean and its resources must be accompanied by a considerable improvement in the mechanisms set down for regulating these activities.

There is already a bewildering variety of international organizations concerned with ocean science or the utilization of ocean resources. I have mentioned the numerous intergovernmental fishery organizations. Within the UN system are the UN itself, its Development Program, its Committee on the Peaceful Uses of the Sea-Bed (dealing with social, economic and political problems and the development of marine resources), UNESCO and its Intergovernmental Oceanographic Commission (scientific investigation of the ocean), the Food and Agriculture Organization (development of fishery research and resources) and the World Meteorological Organization (meteorological aspects of ocean research and services). Intergovernmental organizations outside the UN system include the International Hydrographic Organization (coordination of hydrographic services) and regional groups such as the International Council for the Exploration of the Sea (principally the North Atlantic and adjacent seas) and the International Commission for the Scientific Exploration of the Mediterranean Sea.

Nongovernmental scientific organizations form another important category. They include the Scientific Committee on Oceanic Research, the International Association for the Physical Sciences of the Ocean, the International Association of Biological Oceanography and the Commission of Marine Geology, which are all components of the International Council of Scientific Unions. Among their functions are scientific discussion and the providing of advice to governmental bodies.

A field such as oceanography may require a multiplicity of international organizations to meet its complex and diverse requirements. It is certain, however, that progress toward mastery and intelligent use of the ocean domain would benefit from a strengthening, simplification and consolidation of the organizations that now exist.

The Authors
Bibliographies
Index

The Authors

WILLARD BASCOM ("Technology and the Ocean") is president and chairman of Ocean Science and Engineering, Inc. He began his career as a mining engineer but switched to oceanography in 1945 as a research engineer for the University of California—first at Berkeley and later at the Scripps Institution of Oceanography. In 1954 he joined the staff of the National. Academy of Sciences, where he became widely known for his work in organizing and directing the first phase of the Mohole Project to drill in deep water through the earth's crust. Bascom founded Ocean Science and Engineering, Inc., in 1962. The company and its subsidiaries own several scientific-exploration ships and are involved in fishing, ocean engineering work, ship repair, dredging and the design, development and construction of oil-production equipment. Bascom is the author of many scientific and technical papers and the author or editor of three nontechnical books: *A Hole in the Bottom of the Sea, Waves and Beaches* and *Great Sea Poetry.*

SIR EDWARD BULLARD ("The Origin of the Oceans") is professor of geophysics at the University of Cambridge, which he entered as an undergraduate and where he has spent most of his career. He began his professional work there in 1931 as a demonstrator in geodesy. He was an experimental officer with the British Navy during World War II and then returned to Cambridge as a reader in experimental geophysics. In 1948–1949 he was professor of physics at the University of Toronto, and from 1950 to 1955 he was director of the National Physical Laboratory in the United Kingdom. Returning to Cambridge in 1956, he became successively assistant director of research for the university, reader in geophysics and professor of geophysics. He was elected a Fellow of the Royal Society in 1941 and was knighted in 1953.

K. O. EMERY ("The Continental Shelves") is at the Woods Hole Oceanographic Institution, where he is involved in a program sponsored jointly by the institution and the U.S. Geological Survey to study the geological history of the continental shelf and slope from Maine to Florida. Following his departure in 1941 from the University of Illinois, where he had received his bachelor's degree in 1937 and his Ph.D. in 1941, he spent two years with the Illinois State Geological Survey and two years with the Division of War Research of the University of California. From 1945 to 1962 he taught and did research at the University of Southern California, where his work centered on marine geology. During most of that time he also participated in field and laboratory studies by the U.S. Geological Survey of marine geology at Bikini Atoll and other atolls, at Guam and in the Persian Gulf. He went to Woods Hole in 1962; last year he served as dean of graduate studies there.

S. J. HOLT ("The Food Resources of the Ocean") is with the Food and Agriculture Organization of the United Nations, serving temporarily as marine science and fishery coordinator with the United Nations Educational, Scientific and Cultural Organization on leave from his position as director of the Division of Fishery Resources and Exploitation in the Department of Fisheries of the FAO. He was born in London and was graduated from the University of Reading, which in 1966 awarded him a D.Sc. on the basis of his published work. From 1946 to 1953 he was with the British Fisheries Laboratory at Lowestoft, serving also from 1950 to 1953 with the Nature Conservancy in Edinburgh. He has been with the FAO since 1954. Holt writes: "My research has been on animal population dynamics, mainly of fish, with a particular interest in the application of such knowledge to the rational management of international fisheries. I am also concerned with problems of international organization and programming in marine science; with the question of ensuring the participation of small and developing countries in marine research and in its benefits, and with the problems of creating a scientifically competent element in the international civil service."

JOHN D. ISAACS ("The Nature of Oceanic Life") is professor of oceanography and director of marine life research at the Scripps Institution of Oceanography. The titles reflect only a portion of his interests; his others include the mechanism of the heating of the earth's interior, the construction of harbors by atomic explosions and the disposal of radioactive wastes at sea. He was also a member of the group that suggested tethering a satellite to the earth by a cable, which would be attached near the Equator so that energy from the turning of the earth would drive loads up the cable to the satellite; the installation could be used to maintain an observatory or fuel spacecraft or even to support very tall structures on the earth's surface. Isaacs came to oceanography in a roundabout way. He went to college to study engineering but became bored and dropped out. Thereafter he worked as a logger, a fire lookout, a merchant seaman and a commercial fisherman. He returned to college in 1944 and obtained his bachelor's degree in engineering (from the University of California at Berkeley) at the age of 32. He has been at Scripps since 1948.

H. W. MENARD ("The Deep-Ocean Floor") is professor of marine geology at the Institute of Marine Resources and the Scripps Institution of Oceanography of the University of California at San Diego. He received his bachelor's and master's degrees at the California Institute of Technology; in 1949 he obtained his Ph.D. from Harvard University. Since then he has been concerned with marine geology; his work has included participation in 17 oceanographic expeditions, mostly in the Pacific. He has also been a visiting professor at Cal Tech, a Guggenheim Fellow at the University of Cambridge and a staff member of the Office of Science and Technology in Washington. His article is the third he has written for SCIENTIFIC AMERICAN. He is also the author of a forthcoming book, *Anatomy of an Expedition,* describing modern scientific life at sea.

ROGER REVELLE ("The Ocean") is Richard Saltonstall Professor of Population Policy in the Faculty of Public Health at Harvard University and director of the Harvard Center for Population Studies. For many years before going to Harvard in 1964 he was director of the Scripps Institution of Oceanography, which he had joined in 1931 as a research assistant. His work in oceanography has won wide recognition; in 1963 the National Academy of Sciences gave him its Agassiz Medal for "outstanding achievement in oceanography." Revelle has also been active in many other areas: he headed the group that developed a plan for land and water development of the Indus River basin; he was a member of the U.S. delegation to the first Atoms for Peace Conference; he has been a member of several panels of the President's Science Advisory Committee; he was U.S. delegate to the General Assembly of the International Council of Scientific Unions in 1968, and he is vice-president of the American Academy of Arts and Sciences. Revelle was graduated from Pomona College in 1929 and began his career as a teaching assistant there. He received his Ph.D. from the University of California in 1936. At the Scripps Institution he became professor of oceanography in 1948 and director in 1951. From 1958 to 1961 he was also director of the La Jolla campus of the University of California. Between 1961 and 1963 he took a leave of absence to serve as the first science adviser to the Secretary of the Interior. He returned to the University of California in 1963 as University Dean of Research for all campuses. Revelle College, the first of the new colleges established in the University of California at San Diego, was named in his honor by the regents of the university in 1965.

R. W. STEWART ("The Atmosphere and the Ocean") is professor in the department of physics and Institute of Oceanography at the University of British Columbia, chairman of the Physical Oceanographic Commission of the International Association of the Physical Sciences of the Ocean and a Fellow of the Royal Society of Canada. He was graduated from Queen's University in Ontario in 1945 with a degree in engineering physics and took his master's degree there two years later. He received his Ph.D. in 1952 from the University of Cambridge, where he also played lacrosse for the university. From 1955 to 1960, when he was appointed to his present position, he worked at the Pacific Naval Laboratory of the Canadian Defence Research Board, mostly on underwater sound propagation. Stewart writes that he has had "a continuing interest in turbulence, which is probably the only connecting thread through my scientific career," and that he has "also been interested in the teaching of physics at the university level."

EDWARD WENK, JR. ("The Physical Resources of the Ocean"), is executive secretary of the National Council on Marine Resources and Engineering Development, a cabinet-level body consisting of the Vice President, who is chairman, and the heads of the eight Federal agencies with programs in the marine sciences. He describes himself as "a research engineer with experience in marine affairs, laboratory management and public administration." Wenk was graduated from Johns Hopkins University in 1940 with a degree in civil engineering. He studied architecture at Harvard University's Graduate School of Design, received a master's degree in applied mechanics from Harvard in 1947 and obtained his doctorate in civil engineering from Johns Hopkins in 1950. From 1942 to 1956 he was responsible for the U.S. Navy's program of structural research on ships. From 1956 to 1959 he was chairman of the department of engineering mechanics at the Southwest Research Institute, designing while there the deep-diving research submersible *Aluminaut.* In 1959 Wenk joined the Legislative Reference Service of the Library of Congress as the first adviser to Congress on science and technology. He was appointed to the White House staff in 1961 as assistant to the President's science adviser and served as executive secretary of the Federal Council for Science and Technology. From 1964 until he was named to his present position in 1966 he was with the Library of Congress as head of the Science Policy Research Division of the Legislative Reference Service.

WARREN S. WOOSTER ("The Ocean and Man") is professor of oceanography at the Scripps Institution of Oceanography, president of the Scientific Committee on Oceanic Research (a unit of the International Council of Scientific Unions) and chairman of the National Academy of Sciences–National Academy of Engineering committee to study the proposal for an International Decade of Ocean Exploration. Wooster began his career as a chemist, obtaining his bachelor's degree at Brown University in 1943 and his master's degree at the California Institute of Technology in 1947. "After having been out in the world as a naval officer," he writes, "I found the laboratory rather restrictive. I learned that my freshman chemistry professor was at Scripps and decided that oceanography would be an interesting career." Wooster received his Ph.D. in oceanography from Scripps in 1953. He has been affiliated with the institution since 1947 except for a year in Lima as director of investigations for the Council of Hydrobiological Investigations of Peru, which he describes as his "introduction to the world of biogeopolitics," and two and a half years in Paris as director of the Office of Oceanography of the United Nations Educational, Scientific and Cultural Organization and secretary of the Intergovernmental Oceanographic Commission. "I have been principally concerned," he writes, "with trying to understand the relation between the physical environment and the biosphere. This involves studying the physical processes as they occur in the ocean and are influenced by atmospheric events, and their ultimate effect on the primary production of organic matter."

Bibliographies

THE OCEAN

THE INFLUENCE OF SEA POWER UPON HISTORY, 1660–1783. Captain A. T. Mahan. Little, Brown, and Company, 1890.

THE MANILA GALLEON: ILLUSTRATED WITH MAPS. William Lytle Schurz. E. P. Dutton & Company, Inc., 1939.

THE EXPLORATIONS OF CAPTAIN JAMES COOK IN THE PACIFIC AS TOLD BY SELECTIONS OF HIS OWN JOURNALS 1768–1779. Edited by A. Grenfell Price. The Limited Editions Club, 1957.

THE ORIGIN OF THE OCEANS

THE HISTORY OF THE EARTH'S CRUST. Edited by Robert A. Phinney. Princeton University Press, 1968.

SEA-FLOOR SPREADING AND CONTINENTAL DRIFT. Xavier Le Pichon in Journal of Geophysical Research, Vol. 73, No. 12, pages 3661–3697; June 15, 1968.

SEISMOLOGY AND THE NEW GLOBAL TECTONICS. Bryan Isacks, Jack Oliver and Lynn R. Sykes in Journal of Geophysical Research, Vol. 73, No. 18, pages 5855–5899; September 15, 1968.

REVERSALS OF THE EARTH'S MAGNETIC FIELD. Sir Edward Bullard in Philosophical Transactions of the Royal Society of London: Series A, Mathematical and Physical Sciences, Vol. 263, No. 1143, pages 481–524; December 12, 1968.

THE ATMOSPHERE AND THE OCEAN

AN INTRODUCTION TO PHYSICAL OCEANOGRAPHY. William S. von Arx. Addison-Wesley Publishing Company, Inc., 1962.

THE GULF STREAM: A PHYSICAL AND DYNAMICAL DESCRIPTION. Henry Stommel. University of California Press and Cambridge University Press, 1965.

THE INFLUENCE OF FRICTION ON INERTIAL MODELS OF OCEANIC CIRCULATION. R. W. Stewart in Studies on Oceanography, edited by Kozo Yoshida. University of Washington Press, 1965.

ENCYCLOPEDIA OF OCEANOGRAPHY. Edited by Rhodes W. Fairbridge. Reinhold Company, 1966.

DESCRIPTIVE PHYSICAL OCEANOGRAPHY. G. L. Pickard. Pergamon Press, 1968.

THE CONTINENTAL SHELVES

ANCIENT OYSTER SHELLS ON THE ATLANTIC CONTINENTAL SHELF. Arthur S. Merrill, K. O. Emery and Meyer Rubin in Science, Vol. 147, No. 3656, pages 398–400; January 22, 1965.

CHARACTERISTICS OF CONTINENTAL SHELVES AND SLOPES. K. O. Emery in Bulletin of the American Association of Petroleum Geologists, Vol. 49, No. 9, pages 1379–1384; September, 1965.

THE ATLANTIC CONTINENTAL MARGIN OF THE UNITED STATES DURING THE PAST 70 MILLION YEARS. K. O. Emery in The Geological Association of Canada Special Paper No. 4, Geology of the Atlantic Region, pages 53–70; November, 1967.

RELICT SEDIMENTS ON CONTINENTAL SHELVES OF WORLD. K. O. Emery in The American Association of Petroleum Geologists Bulletin, Vol. 52, No. 3, pages 445–464; March, 1968.

THE DEEP-OCEAN FLOOR

HISTORY OF OCEAN BASINS. H. H. Hess in Petrologic Studies: A Volume in Honor of A. F. Buddington, edited by A. E. J. Engel, Harold L. James and B. F. Leonard. The Geological Society of America, 1962.

A NEW CLASS OF FAULTS AND THEIR BEARING ON CONTINENTAL DRIFT. J. Tuzo Wilson in Nature, Vol. 207, No. 4995, pages 343–347; July 24, 1965.

SPREADING OF THE OCEAN FLOOR: NEW EVIDENCE. F. J. Vine in Science, Vol. 154, No. 3755, pages 1405–1415; December 16, 1966.

SEA FLOOR SPREADING, TOPOGRAPHY, AND THE SECOND LAYER. H. W. Menard in Transactions American Geophysical Union, Vol. 48, No. 1, page 217; March, 1967.

RISES, TRENCHES, GREAT FAULTS AND CRUSTAL BLOCKS. W. Jason Morgan in Journal of Geophysical Research, Vol. 73, No. 6, pages 1959–1982; March 15, 1968.

THE NATURE OF OCEANIC LIFE

THE OPEN SEA: THE WORLD OF PLANKTON. Alister C. Hardy. Houghton Mifflin Company, 1957.

THE OPEN SEA: FISH AND FISHERIES. Alister C. Hardy. Houghton Mifflin Company, 1959.

OCEANS: AN ATLAS-HISTORY OF MAN'S EXPLORATION OF THE DEEP. Edited by G. E. R. Deacon. Paul Hamlyn, 1962.

BIOLOGY OF SUSPENSION FEEDING. C. B. Jorgensen. Pergamon Press, 1966.

THE PHYSICAL RESOURCES OF THE OCEAN

THE MINERAL RESOURCES OF THE SEA. John L. Mero. Elsevier Publishing Company, 1965.

MINERAL RESOURCES OF THE WORLD OCEAN: PROCEEDINGS OF A SYMPOSIUM HELD AT THE NAVAL WAR COLLEGE, NEWPORT, RHODE ISLAND, JULY

11–12, 1968. Edited by Elisabeth Keiffer. Graduate School of Oceanography, University of Rhode Island, Occasional Publication No. 4, 1968.

USES OF THE SEAS. Edited by Edmund A. Gullion. Prentice-Hall, Inc., 1968.

ENCOURAGING DEVELOPMENT OF NONLIVING RESOURCES. *Marine Science Affairs—a Year of Broadened Participation: The Third Report of the President to the Congress on Marine Resources and Engineering Development.* U.S. Government Printing Office, January, 1969.

ENHANCING BENEFITS FROM THE COASTAL ZONE. *Marine Science Affairs—a Year of Broadened Participation: The Third Report of the President to the Congress on Marine Resources and Engineering Development.* U.S. Government Printing Office, January, 1969.

PETROLEUM RESOURCES UNDER THE OCEAN FLOOR. National Petroleum Council, 1969.

THE FOOD RESOURCES
OF THE OCEAN

LIVING RESOURCES OF THE SEA: OPPORTUNITIES FOR RESEARCH AND EXPANSION. Lionel A. Walford. The Ronald Press Company, 1958.

FISHERIES BIOLOGY: A STUDY IN POPULATION DYNAMICS. D. H. Cushing. University of Wisconsin Press, 1968.

MARINE SCIENCE AND TECHNOLOGY: SURVEY AND PROPOSALS. REPORT OF THE SECRETARY-GENERAL. United Nations Economic and Social Council, E/4487, 1968.

THE STATE OF WORLD FISHERIES: WORLD FOOD PROBLEMS, No. 7. Food and Agriculture Organization of the United Nations, 1968.

WORK OF FAO AND RELATED ORGANIZATIONS CONCERNING MARINE SCIENCE AND ITS APPLICATIONS. FAO Fisheries Technical Paper No. 74. Food and Agriculture Organization of the United Nations, September, 1968.

TECHNOLOGY AND THE OCEAN

THE SUBMERSIBLE AS A SCIENTIFIC INSTRUMENT. A. Conrad Neumann in *Oceanology International*, Vol. 3, No. 5, pages 39–43; July–August, 1968.

MARINE SCIENCE AFFAIRS—A YEAR OF BROADENED PARTICIPATION: THE THIRD REPORT OF THE PRESIDENT TO THE CONGRESS ON MARINE RESOURCES AND ENGINEERING DEVELOPMENT. U.S. Government Printing Office, January, 1969.

THE OCEAN AND MAN

INTERGOVERNMENTAL OCEANOGRAPHIC COMMISSION (FIVE YEARS OF WORK). Intergovernmental Oceanographic Commission Technical Series No. 2. UNESCO, 1966.

MARINE SCIENCE AND TECHNOLOGY: SURVEY AND PROPOSALS. REPORT OF THE SECRETARY-GENERAL. United Nations Economic and Social Council, E/4487, 1968.

THE LAW OF THE SEA: INTERNATIONAL RULES AND ORGANIZATION FOR THE SEA. PROCEEDINGS OF THE THIRD ANNUAL CONFERENCE, 1968. Law of the Sea Institute, University of Rhode Island, 1969.

AN OCEANIC QUEST: THE INTERNATIONAL DECADE OF OCEAN EXPLORATION. National Academy of Sciences Publication No. 1709, 1969.

Index

.024

ean

R